Welcome to
Raspberry Pi
The Complete Manual

The Raspberry Pi is one of the most exciting things to happen to computer technology in recent years. As an educational tool, this tiny PC has reignited interest in bare-metal computing in schools and homes all over the world. As a platform for open-source software, it has also inspired millions of people to try Linux – many for the first time. Most exciting of all is the potential to incorporate the device into practical projects, as demonstrated by the tutorials in this new edition of Raspberry Pi The Complete Manual. Grab your Pi and start creating!

Raspberry Pi
The Complete Manual

Future Publishing Ltd
Richmond House
33 Richmond Hill
Bournemouth
Dorset BH2 6EZ
☎ +44 (0) 1202 586200
Website **www.futureplc.com**

Creative Director **Aaron Asadi**

Editorial Director **Ross Andrews**

Editor In Chief **Jon White**

Production Editor **Amy Best**

Senior Art Editor **Greg Whitaker**

Assistant Designer **Steve Dacombe**

Printed by
William Gibbons, 26 Planetary Road, Willenhall,
West Midlands, WV13 3XT

Distributed in the UK, Eire & the Rest of the World by
Marketforce, 5 Churchill Place, Canary Wharf, London, E14 5HU.
☎ 0203 787 9060 www.marketforce.co.uk

Distributed in Australia by
Gordon & Gotch Australia Pty Ltd, 26 Rodborough Road,
Frenchs Forest, NSW, 2086 Australia
☎ +61 2 9972 8800 www.gordongotch.com.au

Future is an award-winning international media
group and leading digital business. We reach more
than 57 million international consumers a month
and create world-class content and advertising
solutions for passionate consumers online, on tablet
& smartphone and in print.

Future plc is a public
company quoted
on the London
Stock Exchange
(symbol: FUTR).
www.futureplc.com

Chief executive Zillah Byng-Thorne
Non-executive chairman Peter Allen
Chief financial officer Penny Ladkin-Brand

Tel +44 (0)1225 442 244

Part of the

book series

Contents

What you can find inside the bookazine

Getting started

The projects

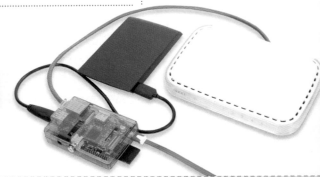

Code & create with your Pi!

"Once you've familiarised yourself with the basics, there's almost
no limit to what you can achieve with your Raspberry Pi"

Raspberry Pi 3

A super-charged Raspberry Pi that finally does everything you'd want it to, for the exact same price as the previous models

While the Raspberry Pi has enjoyed years of success, there's always been a couple of things a lot of users wanted. A slightly more powerful CPU that could handle day-to-day computing, more USB ports and maybe wireless to make connecting to the network easier.

The Raspberry Pi 3 solves these problems. As it uses the same board design as the Model B+, it has four USB ports, as opposed to the two that were on the original Raspberry Pi Model B. More importantly, it has a much more powerful processor and more RAM, making it ten times faster than the original Pi. The Pi 3 has also added built-in wireless capabilities, which makes connecting to Wi-Fi and Bluetooth a cinch.

The new BCM2837 chip is the heart of the Raspberry Pi 3, a modified version of the BCM2836 chip from the old Raspberry Pi 2. The quad-core, 900 MHz processor has been further powered up to become a 1,200 MHz beast, which helps to make the Pi 3 a much more functional board. Whereas before you might have had problems surfing the internet or writing a document, now the Pi 3 breezes through these tasks with ease and plenty of processor power to spare.

At heart though, it's still the same board as the Raspberry Pi B+. As well as the aforementioned four USB 2.0 ports, there's the Ethernet port for wired internet, a good-quality 3.5mm headphone jack for sound, a HDMI port for digital video and audio and a 40-pin GPIO port. This expanded GPIO port is fantastic for making your physical projects even more involved and complicated to do far cooler things.

For those worried about compatibility, all your old files and projects and such work just fine on the Raspberry Pi 3, and all you need to do is transfer them over like any normal files.

GPIO port
The 40 pins in the GPIO port give you a range of power and function slots to control a project or read more data from your surroundings. This makes the Raspberry Pi 3 the perfect core for an Internet of Things or Maker project

USB ports
The four USB ports give you much more flexibility with the Raspberry Pi 3, allowing you to easily add a keyboard, mouse, wireless dongle and external storage without needing to constantly switch out or get a powered-hub

Ethernet port
The Pi 3 retains the wired network and internet connection that was on the Model B of the original Raspberry Pi. It still tops out at 100 MB, but that's plenty fast enough for the Raspberry Pi

Integrated wireless
The big update brought in with the Raspberry Pi 3 is the introduction of built-in 802.11n wireless LAN and Bluetooth 4.1. Connecting to the Internet and other devices has never been easier

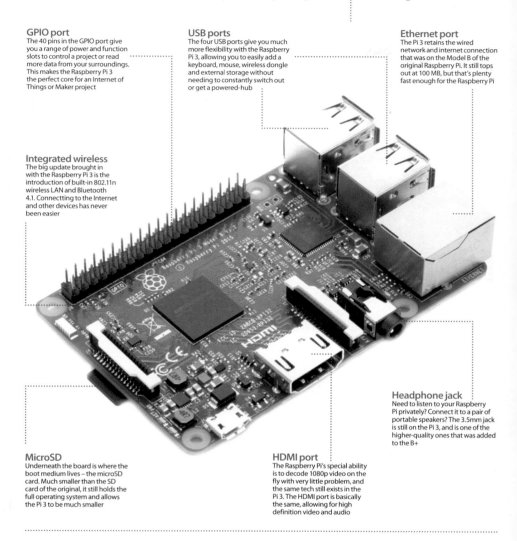

Headphone jack
Need to listen to your Raspberry Pi privately? Connect it to a pair of portable speakers? The 3.5mm jack is still on the Pi 3, and is one of the higher-quality ones that was added to the B+

MicroSD
Underneath the board is where the boot medium lives – the microSD card. Much smaller than the SD card of the original, it still holds the full operating system and allows the Pi 3 to be much smaller

HDMI port
The Raspberry Pi's special ability is to decode 1080p video on the fly with very little problem, and the same tech still exists in the Pi 3. The HDMI port is basically the same, allowing for high definition video and audio

"The Raspberry Pi 3 still won't be able to power a USB hub, so if you need to expand the complement you'll need to get a powered-hub"

Raspberry Pi Model A+

Good things come in small packages: find out why the Raspberry Pi A+ is ideal for mobile projects.

While the Raspberry Pi Model B+ is a step up from the Model B with its four USB ports, the Model A+ is smaller than its predecessor, weighing just 23g (down from 45g) and wielding one USB port. It's also limited to just 256MB of RAM on the SoC, compared to the 512MB enjoyed on the B+.

But don't think that all of this means that the A+ is inferior. Its 65mm length and lower weight is a clue as to how it can be used. The lack of an Ethernet port meanwhile, isn't a weakness, rather an illustration of the fact that this Raspberry Pi is designed not for media centres and print servers, but for projects where weight is a factor. Perhaps you'll mount it on an Arduino-powered robot, where its lower power requirement can be satisfied with a battery.

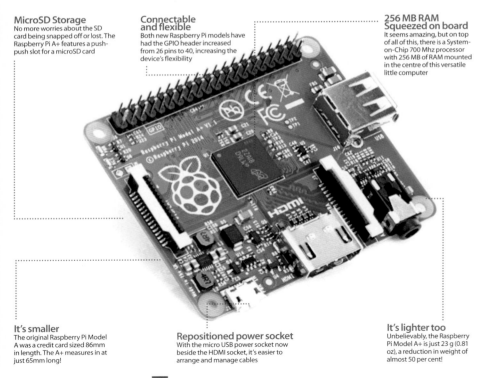

MicroSD Storage
No more worries about the SD card being snapped off or lost. The Raspberry Pi A+ features a push-push slot for a microSD card

Connectable and flexible
Both new Raspberry Pi models have had the GPIO header increased from 26 pins to 40, increasing the device's flexibility

256 MB RAM Squeezed on board
It seems amazing, but on top of all of this, there is a System-on-Chip 700 Mhz processor with 256 MB of RAM mounted in the centre of this versatile little computer

It's smaller
The original Raspberry Pi Model A was a credit card sized 86mm in length. The A+ measures in at just 65mm long!

Repositioned power socket
With the micro USB power socket now beside the HDMI socket, it's easier to arrange and manage cables

It's lighter too
Unbelievably, the Raspberry Pi Model A+ is just 23 g (0.81 oz), a reduction in weight of almost 50 per cent!

Raspberry Pi Zero

The tiny £4 computer has taken the world by storm, but what's changed?

Coming in at a size smaller than a credit card, the Pi Zero is certainly impressive to behold. However, its size does not mean a scale back in performance. The Zero's 1Ghz, Single-core CPU and 512MB RAM has this board running 40% faster than the original Pi.

To achieve such a small form factor and low production costs, the creators stripped back a lot of ports we have come to expect. With only space saving micro and mini ports remaining and no Ethernet in sight, adapters of various kinds will play a vital role in more demanding projects. By ensuring every component is justified in its existence, the Pi Zero is incredibly versatile. Its capability to run full images such as Raspbian, means jumping into a project is as simple as ever.

The minimalism of the Zero lends itself perfectly to running in a headless setup, add a Wi-Fi dongle and you can SSH in to control it, making the most of that single USB port.

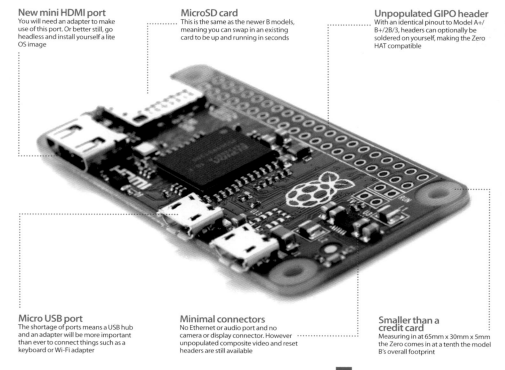

New mini HDMI port
You will need an adapter to make use of this port. Or better still, go headless and install yourself a lite OS image

MicroSD card
This is the same as the newer B models, meaning you can swap in an existing card to be up and running in seconds

Unpopulated GIPO header
With an identical pinout to Model A+/B+/2B/3, headers can optionally be soldered on yourself, making the Zero HAT compatible

Micro USB port
The shortage of ports means a USB hub and an adapter will be more important than ever to connect things such as a keyboard or Wi-Fi adapter

Minimal connectors
No Ethernet or audio port and no camera or display connector. However unpopulated composite video and reset headers are still available

Smaller than a credit card
Measuring in at 65mm x 30mm x 5mm the Zero comes in at a tenth the model B's overall footprint

The starter kit

There's more to your Pi than first meets the eye. Here are some vital peripherals to get you started

In order to get the very best experience from your Raspberry Pi, you're going to have to get hold of a few extras on top of the actual Raspberry Pi board itself. For example, you're going to need a keyboard and mouse with which to enter commands and navigate. While it's possible to do projects without a keyboard and mouse attached, you'll need them for the initial setup. An SD card is also an important purchase – it's where the operating system lives.

Perhaps you'll need a Wi-Fi adapter, or maybe just a length of network cable. Then there's the basic electronics side of the Raspberry Pi, what would you need to start some of the beginner electronics and control experiments? Clearly, there's more to the Raspberry Pi than some might think.

By 'peripherals', we mean other hardware that can be attached and utilised by the Raspberry Pi. They could be something as simple as a decent HDMI or they could be the latest, greatest bespoke gadgets that enhance your project capabilities.

There is an entire world of possibilities available for the Raspberry Pi; from robot arms to remote-controlled helicopters… The only limits are the hardware available and your imagination.

Did you know…

Most online retailers sell packages complete with all the accessories you might need – even pre-installed SD cards.

Keyboard and mouse

Let's start with the most basic of components, the keyboard and mouse. Generally speaking, virtually any USB keyboard and three-button scroll mouse will work with the Raspberry Pi, and although for some projects you won't even need a keyboard and mouse, you'll need them for initial setup.

SD card

Early Raspberry Pi computers required an SD card, whereas later models such as the Raspberry Pi 2 and 3 use microSD cards for storage. This is where your chosen operating system (such as Raspbian) is installed, and these can be bought in various sizes, pre-installed with the OS, or blank.

Power cable

The Raspberry Pi uses a standard micro USB connector for its power input, running at 5V. In most cases a micro USB to USB cable will suffice, of which one end can be plugged into your desktop computer's USB port. An Android phone charger should also work perfectly (5.25V 1500mA).

Case

Securing your Raspberry Pi in a case will protect it and prevent the delicate GPIO pins from accidental damage. A case can also make your Raspberry Pi a more attractive or striking unit, perhaps as a media centre. Ensure you choose the right case for your Raspberry Pi model.

Video output

There are two video output ports, a HDMI port and an RCA Socket. HDMI is the primary video-output connector for most users, but the RCA video-out port can also be used to connect TVs, monitors or to a SCART cable. Remote access to your Raspberry Pi is also possible via SSH or VNC.

Powered USB hub

Extra USB ports are worth considering as an early purchase with your Pi. Once you've connected a keyboard and mouse you'll realise why! Using a powered USB hub is important, to stop any power being drained from the Pi, and allow you to attach the likes of an external hard drive, for example.

Raspberry Pi camera board

This is a custom designed add-on board that attaches to one of the Raspberry Pi's on-board sockets via a flexible cable. It's extremely small, but remarkably powerful, having a native resolution of five megapixels and supporting 1080p video. It's essentially a smartphone camera for the Pi.

USB Wi-Fi adaptor

Using a USB Wi-Fi adaptor will bring flexibility to where you position your Raspberry Pi. Without a restrictive Ethernet cable, it could be used for more advanced projects where running a wired internet connection isn't a valid option. Just make sure you buy a Raspberry Pi-friendly Wi-Fi adaptor.

Set up your Raspberry Pi

Learn what goes where in your brand new Raspberry Pi with our easy-to-follow guide

While it looks daunting, setting up the Raspberry Pi for day-to-day use is actually very simple. Like a TV or a normal computer, only certain cables will fit into the specific slots, and the main job really is making sure you've got plugged in what you need at any one time. The Raspberry Pi itself doesn't label much of the board. However, most good cases will do that for you anyway – if you decide to invest in one.

Power adapter
The Raspberry Pi is powered using a micro USB cable, much like a lot of modern Android phones. It can be powered off a laptop or computer. But to make the most out of it, a proper mains adapter – like this one – is ideal

Monitor
The Raspberry Pi is capable of displaying a 1920 x 1080 output – otherwise known as 1080p. Some modern monitors allow you to plug HDMI straight into them, just like TVs do. However you may need an adapter in some cases

USB hub
There are only a limited number of USB ports on a Raspberry Pi (just one, if you have Model A). To get around this you will need a USB hub. It's important to get a powered one, as the Pi cannot supply enough juice on its own

Case and accessories
A case is not necessary to use the Pi correctly, but a decent one can keep it well protected from dust, and make it easier to move while in operation. You will need an SD card, however, of at least 4GB

Keyboard and mouse
Like any computer, you'll need a keyboard and mouse for any standard PC-style operations you do with the Raspberry Pi. The more basic the keyboard, the better; same with the mouse, as some special ones need additional software

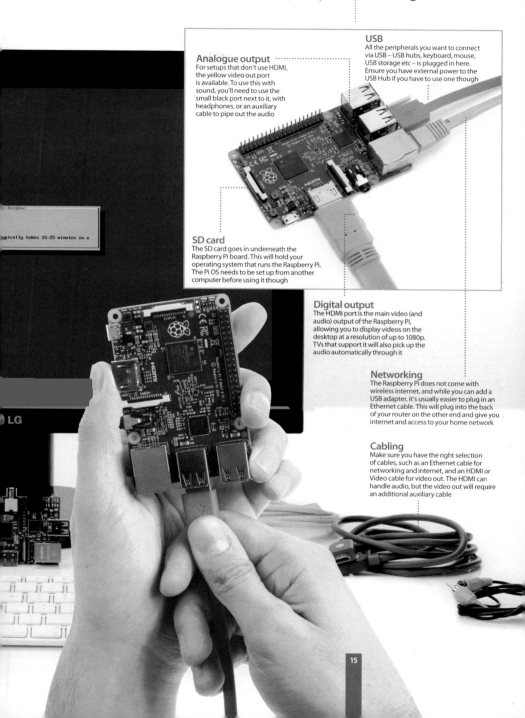

USB

All the peripherals you want to connect via USB – USB hubs, keyboard, mouse, USB storage etc – is plugged in here. Ensure you have external power to the USB Hub if you have to use one though

Analogue output

For setups that don't use HDMI, the yellow video out port is available. To use this with sound, you'll need to use the small black port next to it, with headphones, or an auxiliary cable to pipe out the audio

SD card

The SD card goes in underneath the Raspberry Pi board. This will hold your operating system that runs the Raspberry Pi. The Pi OS needs to be set up from another computer before using it though

Digital output

The HDMI port is the main video (and audio) output of the Raspberry Pi, allowing you to display videos on the desktop at a resolution of up to 1080p. TVs that support it will also pick up the audio automatically through it

Networking

The Raspberry Pi does not come with wireless internet, and while you can add a USB adapter, it's usually easier to plug in an Ethernet cable. This will plug into the back of your router on the other end and give you internet and access to your home network

Cabling

Make sure you have the right selection of cables, such as an Ethernet cable for networking and internet, and an HDMI or Video cable for video out. The HDMI can handle audio, but the video out will require an additional auxiliary cable

15

What you'll need…

Raspberry Pi Zero

Micro USB power supply

Soldering iron and solder

Pi Zero adaptor bundle

Monitor, mouse and keyboard
Optional

USB Wi-Fi or USB Ethernet adaptor
Optional

USB hub
Optional

Set up your Pi Zero

Get to grips with your Raspberry Pi Zero, either as a headless device or for use together with a screen and keyboard

So you've picked up one of the tiny yet powerful Zeros, but before the coding fun can begin you need to get more familiar with it. Don't worry; we'll walk you through the Raspberry Pi Zero, the required cables, how to prepare a NOOBS SD card, and how to solder the GPIO header onto the Pi. Once the Pi is working and booted we'll show you how to get it working on Wi-Fi through the Raspbian user interface. You'll need a USB hub for this, or even just to use a keyboard and mouse together. We'll also show you how to prepare a Raspbian SD card for headless use (either VNC or SSH) with only a Wi-Fi adapter or USB-to-Ethernet adaptor.

Raspberry Pi Zero Cable Overview

01 The Raspberry Pi Zero is very small, and as such cannot fit normal-sized USB and HDMI connectors on. To use it, you therefore need adaptors that break out micro USB into full-size USB and mini HDMI to full-size HDMI. You also need to be very careful when connecting the micro USB cables as the micro USB power cable will fit into the connector meant for USB data. It's easy to tell them apart though, as they're clearly labelled, and the USB data connector can be found between the HDMI and power connectors.

Fig 1: Once you've soldered the header into place, your Pi Zero should resemble any other Raspberry Pi

GPIO header

02 Soldering your brand new Raspberry Pi Zero might seem like a scary prospect at first, but it's not that difficult! What is difficult, however, is snapping off the correct number of GPIO header pins (40), as the kit supplies more than 40. It's also well worth noting at this point that it doesn't matter too much if you mess up and end up missing a couple of the bottom pins.

Soldering kits

03 Soldering irons are very cheap these days. If you are going to be doing a lot of soldering then it's probably worth getting a temperature-controlled one where you can change the tip. However,

the kit we used with a soldering iron, stand, solder sucker and some lead-free solder was £8 on Amazon. We managed to solder the GPIO pins using this kit no problem.

Holding the GPIO headers in place

04 Before you can solder the GPIO headers, you need to be able to hold them in place. We recommend putting some blu-tack on either side of the pins for this. This also has the advantage that you can flip the Pi over and then use the blu-tack to keep it in place on a table while you are soldering. The blu-tack should just easily peel off once you are done.

Solder the GPIO headers

05 Here comes the bit you might have been dreading, but don't worry! Make sure you have wet the sponge in the soldering iron holder, as you will need to wipe the iron on the sponge to keep the tip clean. If this is the first time your iron has been used, the heating element will probably give off a lot of smoke for

the first few minutes, so don't worry if that happens. Still, be mindful of your safety and make sure that you are soldering in a well-ventilated area – try not to breathe in any fumes. Once the iron is hot, apply some solder to the tip and wipe any excess solder on the sponge. Then start to solder the pins. For each pin, touch the tip of the iron on the bottom of the GPIO header and the metal contact on the Pi, then apply a very small amount of solder. Once the solder has flowed onto the pin and the metal contact, then you can remove the iron. If there is too much solder then you can reheat the solder and use the solder sucker to remove it. Take breaks when soldering the GPIO headers for a couple of reasons: 1) you don't want to overheat any components on the Pi, and 2) you can melt the plastic of the GPIO headers and that will allow the pin to fall through. Keep wiping the tip of the iron on the sponge to keep it clean throughout the soldering process. Make sure you unplug the iron and put it somewhere safe to cool down when you are finished.

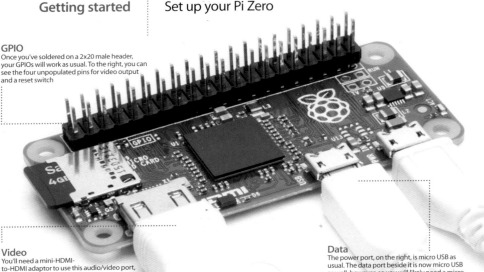

GPIO
Once you've soldered on a 2x20 male header, your GPIOs will work as usual. To the right, you can see the four unpopulated pins for video output and a reset switch

Video
You'll need a mini-HDMI-to-HDMI adaptor to use this audio/video port, although you can also use the RCA composite video output via the unpopulated pin

Data
The power port, on the right, is micro USB as usual. The data port beside it is now micro USB as well, however, so you will likely need a micro USB-to-USB adaptor

Prepare NOOBS SD Card

06 See www.raspberrypi.org/help/noobs-setup for more details. NOOBS requires an SD card formatted as FAT32. You then need to download the latest NOOBS image from https://downloads.raspberrypi.org/NOOBS_latest and then unzip it to the SD card. On Linux, the steps are as follows:

```
sudo parted /dev/mmcblk0
(parted) mktable msdos
(parted) mkpart primary
fat32 0% 100%
(parted) quit
sudo mkfs.vfat /dev/
mmcblk0p1
cd /mnt
sudo mkdir pi
sudo mount /dev/mmcblk0p1 pi
cd pi
sudo unzip ~/Downloads/
NOOBS_v1_5_0.zip
sync
cd ..
sudo umount pi
```

Boot NOOBS and install Raspbian

07 Connect your Pi Zero up as shown in the first step. The minimum you need connected for a NOOBS install is a monitor and a keyboard. However, a mouse and either an Ethernet adaptor or Wi-Fi adaptor are also very useful. Press Enter to select Raspbian and then press I to install. Then press Enter to agree. Once it is finished it will say 'OS installed successfully'. Press OK and your Pi will reboot into Raspbian. Alternatively, if you don't want to use NOOBS, you can flash Raspbian to an SD card in the usual manner. Raspbian will boot into a desktop environment by default.

Configure Wi-Fi

08 If you are using a USB-to-Ethernet adaptor then the Pi should already be connected to the internet. If you are using a Wi-Fi adapter then you will need to configure it to connect to your wireless network. We are using an Edimax EW-7811UN, which works

perfectly with the Pi out of the box. Once at the Raspbian desktop, you can click on the network icon in order to see the available wireless networks. Once you click on one it will ask you for the password. After that it should be associated; you can hover your mouse over the icon and see the networks that you are connected to.

Configure Wi-Fi from another machine

09 If you want to use the Pi Zero as a headless device with Wi-Fi then you can prepare an SD card using another Linux machine that will already be configured to connect to the correct Wi-Fi network. You have to mount the SD card and edit /etc/wpa_supplicant/wpa_supplicant.conf, which is the same file that is configured by the

Raspbian user interface from the previous step. Insert the SD card into your Linux machine and work out what the device is called.

▌ dmesg | tail -n 3

▌ [320516.612984] mmc0: new high speed SDHC card at address 0001

▌ [320516.613437] mmcblk0: mmc0:0001 SD8GB 7.35 GiB

So the device is /dev/mmcblk0 – now we need to work out which partition number the root partition is (this will be different on a Raspbian image; we are using a NOOBS image here).

▌ sudo parted /dev/mmcblk0 print

This will give you a list of the partitions. The largest partition will be the root partition. In this case it's partition 7, so the root filesystem is at /dev/mmcblk0p7. To mount the SD card and edit the wpa_supplicant.conf file do the following

▌ cd /mnt

▌ sudo mkdir pi

▌ sudo mount /dev/mmcblk0p7 pi/

▌ cd pi/

▌ sudo nano etc/wpasupplicant/wpa_supplicant.conf

Then fill in your Wi-Fi details:

▌ network={
▌ ssid="your_wifi_network"
▌ psk="your_wifi_password"
▌ key_mgmt=WPA-PSK
▌ }

Then finally:

▌ cd ..

▌ sudo umount pi/

Remotely access your Pi

10 You can use nmap to scan the local network to find a Raspberry Pi. You need to know the address range of your local network (common networks are 192.168.1.0/24, and 192.168.2.0/24). You can find it with the ip addr command. nmap

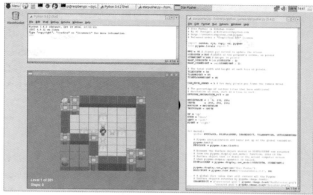

Fig 2: The Zero may be tiny but it is just as good for programming

-p22 -sV 192.168.157.0/24 will scan for a list of devices with SSH open. Example output:

▌ Nmap scan report for 192.168.157.29

▌ Host is up (0.070s latency).

▌ PORT   STATE SERVICE VERSION

▌ 22/tcp open   ssh (protocol 2.0)

Then you can SSH in with:

▌ ssh pi@192.168.157.29

The password is 'raspberry'. If you are using the Pi headless, you'll want to disable the user interface that is started on boot by default:

▌ sudo systemctl set-default multi-user.target

Setup a VNC server

11 VNC stands for Virtual Network Computing. Using VNC you can access the Raspbian desktop over the network (meaning you only need power and Ethernet/Wi-Fi

connected). There is no audio support, but for any other tasks (including the use of pygame) VNC should provide an acceptable level of performance. You can install a VNC server with the following commands

▌ sudo apt-get update

▌ sudo apt-get install tightvncserver

There are several free VNC clients available so a search engine will help you find a suitable one. To start a VNC session on your Pi, log in over SSH and then run tightvncserver. You will be prompted to enter a password the first time you run it. You can specify a screen resolution with the -geometry option: for example, -geometry 1024x768. You can kill an existing vnc session with tightvncserver -kill :1, where 1 is the session number. To connect to that session on a Linux machine, you could use the command: vncviewer 192.168.157.29:1, substituting for the IP address of your Raspberry Pi.

"The minimum that you need connected for a NOOBS install is a monitor and a keyboard"

What you'll need…
....

Raspberry Pi downloads
www.raspberrypi.org/downloads

Install a distro

We take a look at some of the key aspects
involved in installing a pre-built OS

With its small size and cheap price, many people might be fooled
into thinking that the Raspberry Pi is only usable for basic tasks, and
learning to program on. While one of the primary goals of the Pi
was to increase computer literacy at a lower level rather than just
learning how to create Excel spreadsheets, the Pi has many other
great uses.

As the Raspberry Pi is essentially a mini PC, with an HDMI and
analog TV output rather than a traditional monitor connection, it
can perform many common tasks that a laptop or desktop is often
used for. While it doesn't really have the processing power or RAM
to run the latest version of Windows, there are other options.

There are a wealth of fully fledged operating systems, many
forked from their desktop big brothers that have been optimised
specifically for the Pi. One of the most popular of these is Raspbian,
which is a port of Debian. Debian is a key part of the Linux
ecosystem, and many other popular open source distributions
are forked from the Debian source code. The original Debian was
released in 1993, and it's come a long way since. Raspbian needed
work to get performance levels up to standard, as the Pi uses the
older ARMv6 architecture. It's now a great everyday desktop.

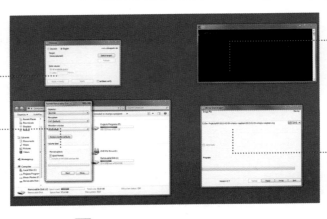

Card speed
It's a good idea to
get a reasonably
fast SD card to keep
your system running
smoothly. Class 4 or
above is best

Command line
If you are using OS X or
Linux, then its likely you
will use the command
line to install your prebuilt
operating systems

Card format
Before you copy
your OS image,
you'll need to make
sure the SD card is
formatted into the
FAT32 file system

Automated tools
There are a couple of
graphical tools available
which make installing
an image onto an SD
card easy

Obtaining OSs

01 One of your first questions may be "where can I find some operating systems to download?". Most of the common images can be found on the main Raspberry Pi site: **www.raspberrypi.org/downloads**. These are stable and well tested systems worth investigating.

Unzipping

02 When you've downloaded your image, the first thing you'll most likely need to do is unzip it. This can be done in Windows by right clicking and choosing 'extract'. In OS X, just double click to extract the files.

OS Format

03 Within the zip you'll find a file with a .img or .iso extension. These are the equivalent of a 'snapshot' of an installation CD or DVD. Simply copying the file to the SD card won't do anything; you'll need to use a program to extract it.

SD card format

04 The SD card that you'll boot from needs to be blank, so make sure there is nothing important on it first. You'll also need to format it to use the FAT32 file system. This is a common system, used by most USB sticks and cameras.

Formatting the card

05 In Windows, to format the card simply insert and wait for it to mount. Then click on 'My Computer' and then right click on the cards icon. After that choose format and then 'FAT32' from the drop-down menu.

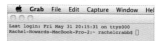

Using the terminal

06 If you are using OS X or Linux, then you'll have to use the terminal to copy the image. In OS X, the Terminal app comes installed by default, and most Linux versions come with one in some form or other. It may be referred to as the 'console' or 'command line'.

DD command

07 The command you need to use is called 'dd'. This is entered in the format of 'sudo dd bs=1m if=[img] of=/dev/[sdcard]'. Eg:

```
sudo dd bs=32m if=/Users/
rachelcrabb/Desktop/ArchLinux/
archlinux-hf-2013-02-11.img
of=/dev/disk1
```

Win 32 Disk Imager

08 Windows users can use Win32 Disk Imager. Once you've downloaded the tool, simply right click on the .exe, and choose 'run as administrator' and follow the prompts. When the installation is complete you can put the SD card in your Pi. Easy!

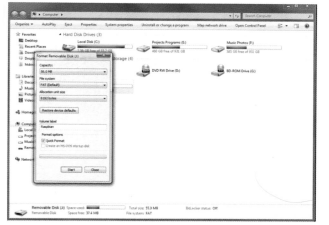

Getting started

What you'll need...

Raspbian
www.raspberrypi.org

Command line basics

Learn an alternative way to control your Raspberry Pi by using the command line and your keyboard

We've probably all been there with the Raspberry Pi. You've installed Raspbian or another Raspberry Pi OS to your SD card and you've rushed through the setup script or not quite done your research. You start the operating system and… you end up at a command line. The first step here is to not panic: this is perfectly normal. It may just be a bit of a foreign concept to you, only seen in films with streetwise hackers who want to bring down 'the system'.

The second step, at least in Raspbian's case, is simply to type:

```
$ start x
```

That's it. Raspbian will load up the desktop and you can start using the mouse again. Quick and painless in this case, and in that of many other operating systems as well. What you've done is use a command, specifically in this case to start the X server. The X server handles the graphical interface and can be turned off by default on some Pi systems.

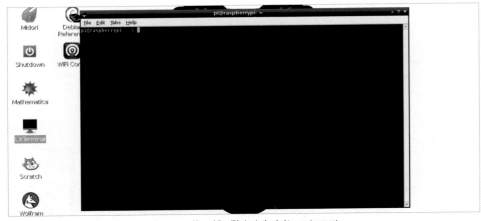

Fig 1: The terminal emulator allows you to access the command line while still being in the desktop environment

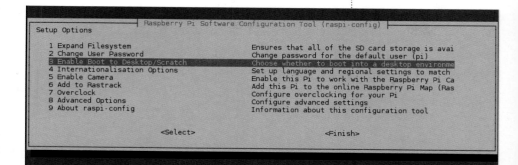

```
┤ Raspberry Pi Software Configuration Tool (raspi-config) ├
Setup Options

   1 Expand Filesystem            Ensures that all of the SD card storage is avai
   2 Change User Password         Change password for the default user (pi)
   3 Enable Boot to Desktop/Scratch   Choose whether to boot into a desktop environme
   4 Internationalisation Options Set up language and regional settings to match
   5 Enable Camera                Enable this Pi to work with the Raspberry Pi Ca
   6 Add to Rastrack              Add this Pi to the online Raspberry Pi Map (Ras
   7 Overclock                    Configure overclocking for your Pi
   8 Advanced Options             Configure advanced settings
   9 About raspi-config           Information about this configuration tool


                <Select>                        <Finish>
```

Fig 2: Access raspi-config to change settings such as boot to desktop or adding a camera module

A new world

Getting your Raspberry Pi into the desktop isn't the only thing you can do on the command line, though. There's a whole world of functionality built into the command line; in fact, most of the graphical programs you're using are just executing these commands in such a way. You don't have to leave the comfort of the desktop environment to perform these commands either, as all Raspberry Pi operating systems will come with an application known as a terminal emulator.

This creates a window where a command can be written in the same way that we launched the desktop, and use the exact same commands (Fig 1). On Raspbian, look for the app LX Terminal in the Accessories section of the menu and click on it. If you've had to use **start x** to get into the desktop, then we can now fix that before continuing. In the terminal, enter:

```
$ raspi-config
```

Here's the initial setup screen (Fig 2). From here you can enable the desktop on boot (Fig 3), and even update the firmware and add support for the official Raspberry Pi camera module. This allows you to modify Raspbian without having to reinstall again.

You won't be using those two commands very often, though, so is there practical use for delving into the command line? Very much so. For starters, Raspbian doesn't have an official package manager. This is a program that allows you to browse the available software for the operating system, similar to the Pi Store.

However, there's other software available to Raspbian that you can't get through the store. You also can't specifically update the Pi software either, and all of this can be fixed using the command line.

Fig 3: Change the default selection to desktop for the next time you use the Raspberry Pi

```
                          pi@raspberrypi: ~                        _ □ x
File  Edit  Tabs  Help
Do you want to continue [Y/n]? y
Get:1 http://mirrordirector.raspbian.org/raspbian/ wheezy/main dpkg armhf 1.16.12+rpi1 [2,583 kB]
Get:2 http://mirrordirector.raspbian.org/raspbian/ wheezy/main curl armhf 7.26.0-1+wheezy8 [267 kB]
Get:3 http://mirrordirector.raspbian.org/raspbian/ wheezy/main libcurl3 armhf 7.26.0-1+wheezy8 [315 kB]
Get:4 http://mirrordirector.raspbian.org/raspbian/ wheezy/main libcurl3-gnutls armhf 7.26.0-1+wheezy8 [306 kB
]
Get:5 http://mirrordirector.raspbian.org/raspbian/ wheezy/main libyaml-0-2 armhf 0.1.4-2+deb7u2 [49.3 kB]
Get:6 http://mirrordirector.raspbian.org/raspbian/ wheezy/main dpkg-dev all 1.16.12+rpi1 [1,349 kB]
Get:7 http://mirrordirector.raspbian.org/raspbian/ wheezy/main libdpkg-perl all 1.16.12+rpi1 [953 kB]
Get:8 http://mirrordirector.raspbian.org/raspbian/ wheezy/main libxfont1 armhf 1:1.4.5-3 [145 kB]
Fetched 5,968 kB in 7s (787 kB/s)
(Reading database ... 68759 files and directories currently installed.)
Preparing to replace dpkg 1.16.12 (using .../dpkg_1.16.12+rpi1_armhf.deb) ...
Unpacking replacement dpkg ...
Processing triggers for man-db ...
Setting up dpkg (1.16.12+rpi1) ...
(Reading database ... 68759 files and directories currently installed.)
Preparing to replace curl 7.26.0-1+wheezy7 (using .../curl_7.26.0-1+wheezy8_armhf.deb) ...
Unpacking replacement curl ...
Preparing to replace libcurl3:armhf 7.26.0-1+wheezy7 (using .../libcurl3_7.26.0-1+wheezy8_armhf.deb) ...
Unpacking replacement libcurl3:armhf ...
Preparing to replace libcurl3-gnutls:armhf 7.26.0-1+wheezy7 (using .../libcurl3-gnutls_7.26.0-1+wheezy8_armhf
.deb) ...
Unpacking replacement libcurl3-gnutls:armhf ...
Preparing to replace libyaml-0-2:armhf 0.1.4-2 (using .../libyaml-0-2_0.1.4-2+deb7u2_armhf.deb) ...
Unpacking replacement libyaml-0-2:armhf ...
Preparing to replace dpkg-dev 1.16.12 (using .../dpkg-dev_1.16.12+rpi1_all.deb) ...
Unpacking replacement dpkg-dev ...
Preparing to replace libdpkg-perl 1.16.12 (using .../libdpkg-perl_1.16.12+rpi1_all.deb) ...
Unpacking replacement libdpkg-perl ...
Preparing to replace libxfont1 1:1.4.5-2 (using .../libxfont1_1%3a1.4.5-3_armhf.deb) ...
Unpacking replacement libxfont1 ...
Processing triggers for man-db ...
```

Fig 4: Upgrade your system and files, and have the latest updates and bug fixes in the process

Software for all

The first thing you'll want to do is let Raspbian know exactly what's available online. It's a very simple task: all you need to do is:

`$ sudo apt-get update`

This will run down a list of online repositories (or repos) that contain the software that Raspbian uses. Once it's finished, the command-line prompt will pop up again waiting for your next command. As this is the first time you've done it, you'll likely need to update the current software on your Raspberry Pi. You can do that with the command:

`$ sudo apt-get upgrade`

It may ask you to confirm the upgrade, in which case type 'y' and then press Enter. What we're doing both times is using the command-line package manager Aptitude (apt-get) to first check the repos, and then upgrade packages according to that (Fig 4). The first command, sudo, allows it to run the apt-get task as an administrator, and is used in a lot of other command-line operations. To install software you use **install** instead of update or upgrade, followed by the name of the package. For example, with the mathematical programming language, you can install it with:

`$ sudo apt-get install wolfram-engine`

Did you know...

You can use the Tab to complete commands. Just start typing and hit tab. If you like what you see hit Enter to finish!

Move and create

Installing and updating are just a couple of the many things you can do in the command line. You can also browse the entire file system, move files, create folders and delete items. All of these are very simple operations.

When you first open the terminal, it will open up in your home folder. While you can't specifically tell that it is, you can display exactly what kind of files are in the directory with (Fig 5):

```
$ ls
```

The tilde sign (~) is used to denote the home folder and can be used for navigating around the file system. To navigate, we'll be using the **cd** command, followed by the location you want to move to. This can be done like so:

```
$ cd /home/pi/Downloads
```

This will move you to the Downloads directory. As we were starting off in the home folder to begin with, we actually only needed to do this:

```
$ cd Downloads
```

It's context sensitive and knows to look in the directory it's already in. There's another trick you can use so you don't have to remember the exact name of the path – the command line or terminal will try to auto-complete the phrase if you press the Tab key while something is only partially typed. Try the cd command again, but try pressing Tab when you've only written 'Down'.

Finally, there are some quick commands you can use to manipulate files. Individual files can be copied using the command **cp**, followed by the filename and the new location like so:

```
$ cp file.txt ~/Documents/file.txt
```

You can also use this to rename files by doing:

```
$ cp file.txt otherfile.txt
```

The original file can then be deleted by using the **rm** command:

```
$ rm file.txt
```

Want to create a new folder? Use cd to move to the directory you need to add a folder to, and then use **mkdir** followed by the name you want to give the folder:

```
$ mkdir NewFolder
```

There's a lot more you can do with the command line, but these are the very basics. As you use Linux more and more, you'll be confronted with tasks that need the command line, and through this process you'll learn just how much can be accomplished when you work like a street-wise movie hacker.

"The command line or terminal will try to auto-complete the phrase if you press the Tab key while something is partially typed"

Fig 5: There are many simple command-line tools that can help you browse and use your system

The Raspbian desktop

Although the Raspberry Pi's Raspbian operating system is closer to the Mac than Windows, it's the latter that the desktop most closely resembles

It might seem a little alien at first glance, but using Raspbian is hardly any different to using a Windows desktop. There's a menu bar, a web browser, a file manager and you'd expect, you simply open the Menu and click the applications you want to get started…

Menu button
The Windows-like Menu button in the top-left corner displays a list of programs and options. The main categories are Programming (where you'll find appropriate tools), Internet (browser and online resources), Games (Minecraft Pi is pre-installed), Accessories (an assortment of utilities), and Preferences (system tools). Programs downloaded from the Pi Store will appear in the appropriate category, while the Run launches a command-line interpreter, just like the one in Windows. Use Shutdown to switch off, logout or restart your Raspberry Pi.

Task Bar
Stripped across the top of the screen is the Task Bar, upon which the Menu is situated. To the right of this are shortcuts to the Epiphany browser, the File Manager (PCManFM), LXTerminal for inputting text-based commands, the Wolfram Mathematica computational software and the Wolfram Language programming application. Next to these shortcuts, you'll find that any open applications are docked, while in the right-hand corner you'll find the clock, current CPU load, volume status and control, and the network status.

File manager
No computer would be complete without a file manager, which can be opened by clicking the Task Bar shortcut. Files can be copied, renamed and deleted by dragging to the trashcan on the desktop (or by simply highlighting and tapping Delete on the keyboard). You can also create tabbed windows in the file browser or open further ones. Folder locations can be bookmarked for easy access and files themselves can be viewed as icons or in a detailed list.

"It might seem a little alien at first glance, but using Raspbian is hardly any different to using Windows"

Web browser

Empathy is the default Raspberry Pi browser, although if you don't like it you can add a new one from the Pi Store. As with any browser, web addresses are typed into the address bar and standard navigation buttons are provided to navigate back and forth through webpages. Empathy supports multiple tabbed windows and features private browsing and the ability to clear browsing data. Click on the Options icon at the end of the tool bar to access these functions.

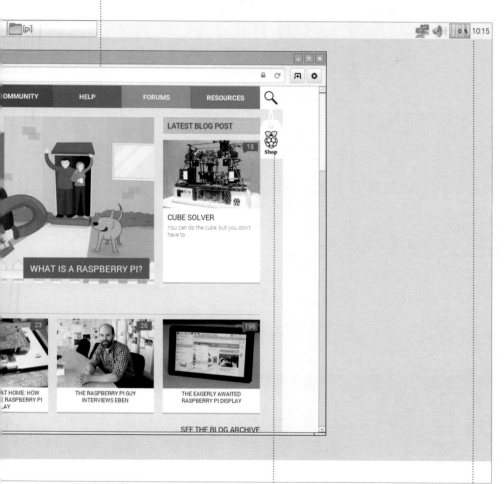

Pi Store

You can access the Pi Store from the Menu, or from a link on the **www.raspberrypi.org** website. Much like Steam, Google Play or the App Store, the Pi Store requires you sign up for an account (with IndieCity), and you'll need to sign in before you begin shopping for free and paid-for software. Any games and apps downloaded and installed from the Store will appear under the My Library tab, and some of those can only be launched from here.

Status and Time

On the far right side of the Task Bar is the Raspbian equivalent of the Windows system tray, where you'll find information concerning your Raspberry Pi's status. In the corner is the clock, which when clicked will also display the current date; if incorrect, you can adjust it here. To the left of this you will find a graph displaying current CPU load, the device volume control, and finally, confirmation that your Raspberry Pi is online.

What you'll need…

Raspbian:
www.raspbian.org

Master the Config tool

Tell your Raspberry Pi how to behave using the powerful built-in Config tool

The 'RasPi Config' tool allows configuration of your system that would otherwise be trickier in the Linux environment and it's the first thing you'll see when you install Raspbian. Why? Tasks such as setting the date and time or regional settings for your keyboard are often done in a command-line interface with no dialogs, no additional help – for a new user, this is a nightmare.

There are some further specifics for the Pi and Raspbian itself, such as: the ability to easily enable overscan for your TV; change the split of memory to the computer/graphics card or even overclock your system to make it a little faster; enable remote SSH access to the system; stop the system booting into the desktop environment among other things. The Raspi Config tool takes the pain out of the process and puts real power at your fingertips.

Change password
Change the password for your default 'pi' username to make it something more personal or easier to remember for you

Expand roots
Allows you to very quickly and easily change the partition of the roots to fill the SD card completely

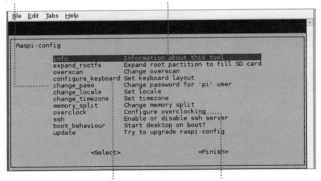

Configure your keyboard
Set the correct keyboard up – there are many different layouts. Using the wrong one can be annoying

Overclocking
Allows you to quickly and easily overclock your Pi to give you some extra speed and power with little risk

Open the raspi-config tool

01 Start by double-clicking the LXTerminal icon on your desktop. This will start the command prompt, where you'll be able to run the config tool. To do this you'll need to run a command.

    sudo raspi-config

When asked for your password, you won't actually see it being typed.

When you've typed the password and pressed Enter to submit it, the config screen will be shown to you. There are a few settings of particular interest that we'll cover in this section, although they all have their uses in the running of your Pi. Some of the settings in this menu are important and some are irreversible, so use them with caution.

Expand the root file system

02 By default, the Raspbian root file system will be 2GB – this is done so that the image provided for it can fit on as many different SD cards as possible.

If your card is larger the 'expand_roots' option will make the OS use the entire space. Upon using this option, the command will be executed immediately. The operating can take some time. Reboot your system to see the changes.

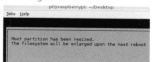

Configure your location

03 Locale is the language and regional settings that your Pi is using – while this generally has little impact on what you'll see, it is also responsible for any default currency settings, etc, so could prove to be an irritant at a later time if wrong.

Upon selecting the option, you'll be taken through a wizard. Use the arrow keys to check the built locale before building more (it takes a while). Timezone will take you to a tzdata screen where you can adjust it.

Overclock your Pi

04 You can set the clock speed and voltage of your Pi to several different presets. Setting the clock speed and voltage at higher rates than the specification may cause instability, so do so in small increments

and ensure good airflow around your Pi.

If you see any noticeable instability, run this wizard again and set the clock speed back down to something slightly lower – repeat until your system is completely stable. For the scope of this tutorial, a Modest/Medium overclock is recommended – it seems to give a little extra performance with no noticeable side effects. It is also recommended to reboot your system after making this change. Hold the Shift key to temporarily disable overclocking.

Change the memory split

05 Changing the memory split of the Pi allows you to give either the system or the graphics processor a larger amount of memory.

The value you give to it must be either 16/32/64/128/256. Here are our recommendations:

32MB GPU memory for basic distro usage where video and 3D rendering aren't required.

64MB GPU memory for desktop use that requires video playback or have 3D effects enabled.

128MB GPU memory for graphical applications and games that do extensive multimedia or play 3D rendered games.

For most people, a 64MB split for graphics will suffice.

Change boot behaviour

06 By default, the Raspbian distro will boot into a command-line interface, whereby you have to first log in as 'pi'.

If you then want to run a window manager (in this case, it's called 'X'), you have to give the system a command to let it know that's what you want to do.

For a lot of people this isn't really ideal since command lines scare them. Because of this, there's an option to

start X automatically, on boot. Set this option to 'Yes' to enable this behaviour by default.

You can obviously revert this at any time to return to a text-based login where you have to start manually:

```
startx
```

Turn overscan on and off

07 You may have noticed one of two behaviours if you're using your Pi with a modern HDTV.

There is a black border the whole way around the image output by the Pi – it just doesn't fit correctly. This is caused by underscan.

If you can't see the edges of your screen to get to them you're suffering from overscan.

If you have the former issue, you may need to either turn on overscan, or enable a 'zoom' mode or similar on your TV.

If you have the latter issue, you need to turn overscan off so that you can see the edges.

Update raspi-config

08 The raspi-config tool receives updates from time to time. This is generally to either add more features or fix small bugs, or both!

It's not a bad idea to run the updater when you use the tool – before you start changing any system settings. While it's much more likely that it'll be updated to look better or do more things, it's not impossible there could be miscellaneous bug fixes hidden within that would otherwise cause you some grief.

Remember, though, when you're trying to update your copy of the raspi-config tool, you'll need an active internet connection, either through an LAN cable or wireless dongle. Without them, it's never going to get any newer. Always try to make sure you're on the latest version.

Did you know...

If your Raspberry Pi is going to be placed near your Internet router, all you need to do is plug in an Ethernet cable.

Get online

To access a world of utilities, apps and resources you need to get online. This is how to do it…

The easiest way to get online is to buy a Raspberry Pi Model B+, as it comes with an Ethernet socket. The Model A not only lacks the Ethernet port, but is handicapped by only having one USB port. That means you will have to buy a power USB hub in order to get online. Back to the Model B+ though and to get online, simply plug an Ethernet cable into the socket on the Pi and connect it to a similar port on the back of your internet modem/router. Turn your Pi on and launch the desktop, then double-click on Empathy and you should see the internet appear (main image). To check that it's working, look at the lights on the Pi itself. The red power light should be on. Above this is the green light that flickers when accessing the SD card. Below the power light are the three Ethernet-related lights. Note that the Model A does not have these LEDs because it doesn't have the Ethernet socket. The middle light is green and comes on when it detects a Full Duplex LAN connection. This means it is able to send and receive data to the internet. The next light is green and flashes when actually accessing the internet by sending or receiving data. The last light is yellow and will come on and stay on when a 100Mb LAN connection is detected.

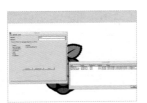

Fig 1: With a Wi-Fi dongle attached, run the utility and scan for available networks

Fig 2: Enter the pre-shared key in order to connect to your home router

The Wi-Fi option

If you aren't close enough to the modem/router to be able to plug in the Ethernet connection, or you simply have a Model A, then a powered USB hub is required. This plugs into a USB port on the Pi. You can then plug a Wi-Fi dongle into this. Boot up the Pi and launch the desktop. Then double-click on the Wi-Fi Config icon. You should see a name for the dongle in the Adapter section. Click on Scan to look for networks and a list of those found should appear (Fig 1). Double-click on the one you want to connect to and the details for it will be listed. Almost all home networks use a network key, which is usually written on the modem itself. Click on PSK, which stands for pre-shared key, and type it in (Fig 2). Then click on Add. It will process this, then associate the connection and then finally, a new IP address for the Wi-Fi connection will appear. If you click on the Manage Networks tab, the network will now be listed and have an Enabled radio button active. To get on the internet, simply launch Empathy and you'll be connected. The Wi-Fi utility will remain running on the bottom right of the panel. If you right-click on the Wi-Fi icon you will see options to Disconnect or Reconnect, event history and the results of the most recent scan. Click on Status to see how it's performing.

Checking the connection
To check that the Pi has a valid internet connection, double-click on LXTerminal. Enter this command:

```
ip addr
```

You should see a list of numbers, with the bottom line starting 'inet' and then the IP address of the Pi connection (Fig 3). Typically this is something like 192.168.1.11 and this shows that the connection is working because the Pi has been assigned an IP address based on the one used by your internet modem/router. If this doesn't come up then there may be a problem at the router end. The modem/router should be running a DHCP server and when the Pi connects to it, it will be given the IP address. If it isn't running then nothing else connected to it will be able to access the internet either. Use the web interface with another device to log onto 192.168.1.0 or whatever is your modem's actual IP address in order to check that the DHCP server service is turned on. Finally, in the terminal, type:

```
ping google.com
```

Sharing a connection
If you don't have a Wi-Fi dongle, a powered USB hub or a long enough Ethernet cable, but do have another computer connected to the internet, there's another way of getting access. On a Mac, connect it to the Pi via a USB or Ethernet cable. Launch System Preferences; under Internet & Wireless, click on Sharing. Click on Internet Sharing, then select Wi-Fi (or AirPort) as the connection type to share, and select how the Pi is connected to your Mac (Fig 4).

On a Windows PC, go to Windows Explorer>Networking> Networking and Sharing Center>Change Adapter Settings.

Fig 3: If it doesn't look like the connection is working, there are some easy ways of checking what's going on

Fig 4: Both Windows and Mac computers can share their internet connections with a directly-connected Pi

Install and use packages

What you'll need…

Apt command help page:
http://linux.die.net/man/8/apt

Apt-get help page:
http://manpages.ubuntu.com/manpages/
lucid/man8/apt-get.8.html

Did you know…

If you press the Tab key the command line will attempt to auto-complete your command for you – just press Enter to finish.

Install and use packages

The Raspberry Pi is great, but it's made better with the software you install onto it

On its own, the Raspberry Pi is a near-perfect mini computer. It already contains a wealth of educational software, a few games, some programming utilities and a number of system tools. But, as with most computers, this is only the tip of the proverbial iceberg. By installing more programs, you can do much more.

These programs, known as packages, are as wide and as varied as the developers who originally designed them. In Linux, if there's a need for a particular program, then someone develops one. They then put it out to the world and make the source code freely available, hence 'open source'. Once the program has been tested, it will eventually make its way onto one of the many remote servers for that particular Linux distro.

These remote servers, called repositories, or repos, contain all the elements of the package in order for it to be downloaded and installed onto your system. The process is very quick and easy once you know how it's done…

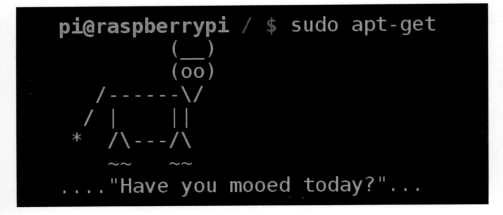

```
pi@raspberrypi / $ sudo apt-get
              (__)
              (oo)
       /-------\/
      / |     ||
     *  /\---/\
        ~~    ~~
    ...."Have you mooed today?"...
```

Update and upgrade

01 Getting hold of a package on the Raspberry Pi involves dropping into the command-line terminal, via the LXTerminal icon on the desktop, and entering a few commands. But before we do that, we need to make sure the system is up to date. Enter the following into the terminal:

```
sudo apt-get update
sudo apt-get upgrade
```
Or…
```
sudo apt-get update && sudo
apt-get upgrade
```

Search for a package

02 The apt-get command (Advanced Package Tool) is the key to downloading and installing packages on the Raspberry Pi. In the previous instance, we updated the existing packages and system, upgraded any that needed it, and updated the current package list. Now, let's search the list of server packages for available games.

```
apt-cache search game | less
```

Apt searching

03 The current list you find yourself in is the name of all the packages labelled as 'games' from the available server. In the list, the part before the hyphen tells you the name of the package, which is what

you will need to know to be able to install it. Use the arrow keys up/down to navigate; press 'Q' to exit.

Installing a package

04 Using the up and down arrow keys, navigate the list. If you find something you like the look of, say Angry Drunken Dwarves, remember the name of the package, in this case 'angrydd', and press 'Q' to exit the list.
To install the package, enter the following in the terminal:

```
sudo apt-get install angrydd
```

Executing the package

05 The result of the previous command should be the successful download and installation of the game, Angry Drunken Dwarves. To execute the newly installed package, you can either run it from the LXDE Menu under Games>Angry Drunken Dwarves, or by typing in the following into the terminal:

```
angrydd
```

Remove a package

06 This installing of packages is perfectly fine, and you can see just how powerful a command Apt really is. But, what if you want to remove a package?
Using the Apt command again, let's say we want to completely remove all trace of Angry Drunken Dwarves from the Raspberry Pi.

```
sudo apt-get --purge remove
angrydd
```
Enter 'Y' to accept the removal.

Apt Easter eggs

07 The Apt command is a shorter, non-menu-driven variant of the Aptitude command. This command has a long history in Linux, and as a result has some rather special 'features', also known as Easter eggs. Purely for a little bit of fun, type in the following commands and see the results:

```
aptitude moo
aptitude -v moo
aptitude -vv moo
aptitude -vvv moo
aptitude -vvvv moo
aptitude -vvvvv moo
aptitude -vvvvvv moo
sudo apt-get moo
```

Man the Apt command

08 As you can see, there is more to the simple Apt command than what first meets the eye. There are many different sub-commands that you can run, and many different variations in which to run them.
If you want to see what else the Apt command can do, enter the following:

```
man apt
```

Use graphical installations

Would you prefer a graphical interface to install new programs? If so, then read on…

What you'll need…

Synaptic:
www.nongnyu.org/synaptic/

Did you know…

Synaptic has access to the same repo as via the command line as demonstrated on the previous two pages.

If you're new to Linux, you may find using its built-in Apt package management tool a bit intimidating and confusing. The apt-get command is used for installing applications through the internet, connecting to the remote servers – called repositories – which house the programs as packages. But it is used through the terminal command prompt, which can be daunting, so we need an alternative: a desktop environment interface method of getting hold of packages.

This is where Synaptic comes in. Synaptic is a friendly-looking graphical interface to the apt-get terminal command which allows you to manage your application installations, and removals, through the already familiar desktop environment. Think of it as a kind of online shop where you can pick and choose the programs you want and have them downloaded and installed onto your Raspberry Pi without you having to drop into the terminal.

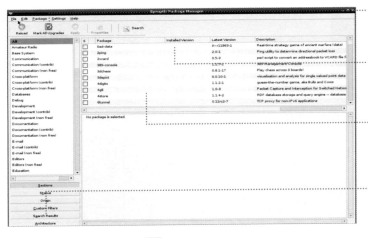

Upgrade entire systems
Synaptic has the ability to update and upgrade every program or package, and it can upgrade your entire system to the latest version

Install and more
Synaptic is a very powerful tool. With it you can install, remove, upgrade and downgrade single or multiple packages and programs

Browse all documentation
From within Synaptic, you are able to browse and read all available online documentation related to a package or program

Easily find programs
Synaptic enables you to easily locate packages and programs by name, description, version and even by who developed the program

Update the system

01 Unfortunately, if you have an aversion to dropping into the command-line terminal, then you're going to be stuck at the first step. Before we install anything, we need to make sure that the Raspberry Pi is fully updated and any existing packages are upgraded. Simply enter the following into the LXTerminal:

■ `sudo apt-get update`
■ `sudo apt-get upgrade`

Installing Synaptic

02 To install Synaptic, you'll first need to enter the LXTerminal and run the command below – don't forget to type Y to any prompts asking you to accept the installation:

■ `sudo apt-get install synaptic`

Running Synaptic – Part 1

03 In essence, that's all you need to do. Synaptic is now installed and ready to use. However, due to its complexity, there may be some bugs that need ironing out first, so it's best to follow these steps. To test if Synaptic is working okay, first enter the following command into the terminal:

■ `gksudo synaptic`

Running Synaptic – Part 2

04 You should be now looking at the Synaptic program window, where you can scroll through the list of available programs and click on each to download and install. Now we need to test whether it will run from the LXDE menu. Click on the icon in the bottom left, then go to Preferences>Synaptic Package Manager.

Running Synaptic – Part 3

05 Running Synaptic from the LXDE menu results in an error. Don't panic, however: all it's doing is asking for a password. Enter the following password into the box:

■ `raspberry`

This is the default Pi password so we're assuming you haven't changed it.

Fixing Synaptic – Option 1

06 This will temporarily fix the issue, but to permanently resolve it, do one of the following. First, right-click the Synaptic icon in

---

the menu and left-click Properties. In the Command text box, change the text to add the gksudo command. So instead of 'synaptic-pkexec', it will read:

■ `gksudo synaptic-pkexec`

Fixing Synaptic – Option 2

07 The second, and best, option is to drop back into the terminal and alter the way in which the program is executed from the menu. All that's needed is to change one line to another, so that the gksudo command is again used instead of the plain synaptic-pkexec. From the terminal, type:

■ `sudo nano /usr/share/ applications/`
■ `synaptic.desktop`

Change 'Exec=synaptic-pkexec' to…

■ `Exec=gksudo synaptic-pkexec`

Synaptic fully working

08 After you've entered those changes, exit nano via Ctrl+X, followed by Y to accept the changes, and then press Enter a couple of times to get back to the command prompt. You can now launch Synaptic from the menu, or by entering the following command when you're in the terminal:

■ `gksudo synaptic`

GPIO port explained

GPIO port explained

What you'll need...

Prototyping equipment
RPi.GPIO
https://pypi.python.org/pypi/RPi.GPIO

Above The Pi's GPIO port comprises 26 pins, used to connect it with all manner of electronic components/devices

GPIO port explained

Learn how to harness the power of the GPIO port on your Raspberry Pi. It's easier than you think...

The general-purpose input/output (GPIO) pins on your Raspberry Pi are often central to the success of the projects you'll find in this book. Without them you have no way of interfacing with the real world, be it to trigger lights, buttons or buzzers or read sensors.

GPIO pins aren't special to the Pi; they're actually a standard designed to help control input and output behaviour with all kinds of integrated circuits. Usually you'll find that any one GPIO pin has no particular use pre-defined and they tend to be turned off by default.

Raspberry Pi GPIO

The GPIO pins on the Raspberry Pi can be controlled and triggered in many ways. You can use them from the terminal directly and through Bash scripts, or you can control them using specially designed modules for popular programming languages. Since Python is the official language of the Raspberry Pi, you'll find the GPIO module for Python gives you among the best control for inputs and outputs available. The library is called RPi.GPIO and is installed by default on all Raspberry Pi, but can otherwise be installed in exactly the same way you'd install any useful Python library. The project is hosted on SourceForge and can be found at **sourceforge.net/projects/raspberry-gpio-python**. You'll also find useful links, information and examples of how to use and control the GPIO pins from within simple Python scripts. It helps to have a basic understanding of Python if you plan to use RPi.GPIO, so we'd recommend a basic introductory course like the one found at **www.codecademy.com** or by reading the official Python documentation at **www.python.org/doc**.

There are 26 GPIO pins on the Raspberry Pi and you can use the vast majority of them in any way you want. There are a few pins that have special purposes, though, so we recommend you familiarise yourself with their layout. For example, the very top row of pins are designed to offer power to external devices like buttons and lights. Since an earth line (often called 'ground') is needed to safely create a circuit, you'll also find several ground pins located in the GPIO port.

How to use GPIO pins

To exploit the power of the GPIO port you'll need a few essential components, the most important of which are jumper leads. Since the pins on the port are 'male', you'll need to purchase either 'female to male' or 'female to female' cables, depending on what hardware you intend to connect to your Pi. Assuming the device you're connecting to also has mail connectors, 'female to female' jumper leads will do nicely, but often you'll be using a breadboard to prototype your circuits, in which case 'female to male' connectors are preferred. Cables and breadboards can be bought very cheaply from just about any online store that sells Raspberry Pi accessories and can usually be found in the 'prototyping' section of the store.

Naming conventions

Once you're ready to connect your device, the next task is to find the right pin for the job. While it's true that all GPIO ports are multipurpose, some are more multipurpose than others! As we've already discovered, some pins are reserved for 5V, 3.3V and ground. Others also have special capabilities, but what's worse is that they can also be called different things. For example, GPIO 18 is also known as pin 12 and PCM_CLK. This particular pin (around halfway down the right side of the GPIO port) is capable of hardware pulse-width modulation (PWM), and is useful for controlling LED lights and motors among other things.

The pin-naming convention you use in your Python scripts can be set manually. This can either be set as BCM (the Broadcom pin name) or the physical pin locations (BOARD).

You'll see in any of the projects where we're using the GPIO port, the following line with either BCM or BOARD in the brackets:

```
GPIO.setmode(GPIO.BCM)
```

The easiest way to deal with the GPIO pin-naming issues is to pick a convention and stick with it.

Below Become familiar with the layout of the GPIO pins and what they do – some have special purposes, such as ground pins

Did you know...

The RPi.GPIO library has some really useful documentation. All you need to do is click on the 'wiki' on Sourceforge.

Top four add-on boards

Get more out of your Raspberry Pi by using these add-on boards to extend its functionality

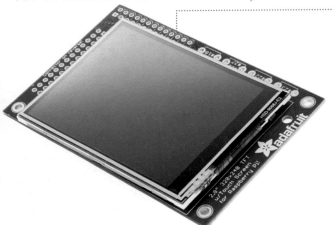

PiTFT Mini Kit £30

This is a 2.8-inch capacitive TFT LCD touchscreen that's been specifically designed with the Raspberry Pi in mind by the project gurus over at Adafruit. It's capable of slotting directly on top of the Raspberry Pi and is about as big as the Pi is itself.

There are numerous reasons why you'd want to add such a screen to a Raspberry Pi but they all generally come down to the fact that the Pi is very small and very portable and most monitors are not. While you could remote connect via VPN from a phone if you're on the go, the screen is connected directly to the Pi and doesn't involve awkward wireless networking. Also as a touchscreen you don't need to bring along other input devices, as it's powered off the Raspberry Pi as well.

This opens it up to a world of possibilities. Portable computer, touchscreen control pad, video camera… anything that could benefit from your Raspberry Pi having a screen and human input while away from your main monitor.

Pi Supply Switch £15

The Raspberry Pi has been so popular, in part, because of the extremely good value for money of the hardware. It packs a lot of punch for the price point and, because it is designed by a charity, they don't need to inflate the price with high profit margins (consider how much it would cost as a commercial product!). Unfortunately, as with anything low-cost, some compromises had to be made in order to bring it in at such an affordable and small form factor.

When comparing it to your more standard desktop or laptop computer, two things that it is obviously lacking are a power switch and power management functionality. It is surprising how something as simple as a power switch can be so very useful, and it is not until you do not have one that you realise this!

The Pi Supply Switch is a self-solder kit which provides an on, off and soft-off (file-safe shutdown) button to give you basic power management functionality for your Pi. With some provided sample scripts you can make sure your Pi is correctly shut down when you switch off – without the need to open any menus or issue any commands in the terminal – and the circuitry in the switch ensures that power is only removed after the Pi has been shut down. As well as making it more convenient for you, it also reduces the possibility of corruption to your SD card from prematurely pulling the power cable.

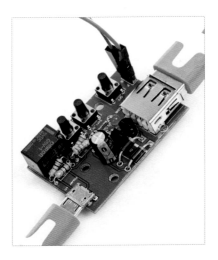

HiFiBerry DAC+ £30

As a high quality audio device, meanwhile, you may find the Raspberry Pi lacking due to the fact it only has a 3.5 mm stereo output that isn't suited to high fidelity. You have probably dreamed of enhancing the audio and taking your setup to the next level. The good news is that the clever folk at the Raspberry Pi Foundation have provided access to the I2S pins; initially on the separate P5 header, and now on the A+, Raspberry Pi 2 and 3 it is available from the main 40-pin GPIO header.

I2S is a communications protocol designed specifically for audio devices and has enabled a number of companies like HiFiBerry and IQaudIO to create high quality audio add-ons. The HiFiBerry DAC+ is an add-on which brings a high resolution (192 kHz, 24-bit) Burr-Brown digital-to-analogue converter to your Pi. It has hardware volume control using Alsamixer, among other features, and as it is a HAT-compatible board. It works plug-and-play out of the box with the latest Raspberry Pi firmwares, and with all the popular operating systems for both standard use and media playback, such as Raspbian, Arch Linux, OSMC, OpenELEC, Volumio, Pi MusicBox and many more. If you are serious about your audio quality and want a high quality, low cost, Internet-connected solution, then you no longer have any excuse – you can build your own for under £100.

"The Energenie Pi-mote control starter kit contains two remote-controlled plug sockets which can be turned on and off"

Energenie Pi-mote £20

Home automation is all the rage at the moment; automating tasks like fiddling with heating controls and turning off the lights before you go to bed can make our lives much easier.

One thing that we are always told is to turn off devices at the plug rather than leaving them on standby, as they use a lot of electricity when not properly turned off. This is where the Energenie Pi-mote control starter kit comes in. It contains two remote-controlled plug sockets which can be turned on and off with an RF remote.

What does this have to do with the Raspberry Pi? Well you also get an add-on board to enable you to control the sockets via software on the Raspberry Pi, which unleashes whole new possibilities – you could set your lamps to turn on and off automatically at specified times when you are away to deter burglars, or create a basic web app to control your plug sockets remotely using your smartphone alone.

They only come in UK and EU plug types, so if you use a different plug then you may need to look for something else (and maybe send Energenie a request to make more versions).

What you'll need…

A second computer
External storage

Did you know…

SD cards don't last forever so always make sure you've got a backup of your files and your entire OS.

Back up your Pi

Take the initiative and back up your Raspberry Pi to make sure you never lose files again

While the Raspberry Pi is a very solid piece of kit, failure can happen, so it's best to be well prepared and keep your files safe.

The good news is that the Pi's files are all kept externally on the SD card. If your Pi breaks, everything will still be available on the SD card and accessible from elsewhere. The SD card is still susceptible to problems, though. There are a number of ways to back up a Pi. The methods can be broken down into two main categories: saving the important files and creating an exact copy of the state of the SD card. The former involves having copies of files elsewhere, while the latter has you create the same kind of image that you'd normally write to the SD card when installing Raspbian or other Pi-operating systems.

Important files

To save important files, we need to create a copy on an external source, such as external hard drive or another PC. One of the best methods to do this doesn't even involve a Pi; all you need is a PC or laptop with a card reader and you're good to go.

Turn off your Pi, unplug it and remove the SD card from the slot. Find the SD card reader on your PC and slot it in. The main file system of the SD card can be read by Linux PCs by default, and a Windows or Mac computer once you've installed a program that lets it read the ext file system, such as Ext2Fsd. On Windows, the SD card will be listed with the rest of the drives under My Computer (Fig 1). On Linux and Mac, it will be listed wherever storage is shown on the menus and file managers.

Once you've found the SD card on here, open it up and navigate to **home** and then **pi**. This is where the Documents, Downloads, Desktop and other directories can be found. All you need to do is select the files you want to copy and move them to a secure directory on your PC or a connected external hard drive.

If you want to keep the files on another computer, that's fine, but it will be prone to the exact same problems as the Pi in the long run. Keeping them on an external hard drive is a good idea, and putting them on a cloud storage service is better yet, enabling you to access them from anywhere with an internet connection (Fig 2).

Cloning

Creating a clone depends on what operating system you're using on your main computer. For Macs and Linux, you can use a simple command-line tool called **dd** to create an exact copy of the SD card (Fig 3). This is done in the terminal emulator or command line, so bring that up first. Make sure the SD card is plugged in and enter:

```
$ fdisk -l
```

This lists all connected storage devices. The SD card will have 2, 4 or 8GB of space, depending on its size. It'll likely be listed as something like **/dev/sd[x]**, where x is the letter the computer attaches to the SD card. To copy it using dd, enter the following into the terminal:

```
$ dd if=/dev/sd[x] of=backup.img bs=1M
```

You can also add a path to the image you're creating to put it in a specific folder. The process will take some time, and will produce a multi-gigabyte file which you can then write onto the SD by reversing the previous command:

```
$ dd if= backup.img of=/dev/sd[x] bs=1M
```

While this is useful as a backup, you can also use the image to mass-produce SD cards to give to friends or keep in the various places where you use your Raspberry Pi.

Windows

To create a clone on Windows, we can use the Win32 Disk Imager (Fig 4). Download it from here to install it: **bit.ly/L8JdYG**.

Once installed, insert the SD card and launch the software. Choose a name for the backup file and select the SD card from the list of devices. Now press Read and it will create the backup file. Again, this might take a while; however, this time you are at least shown a progress bar.

Storing your cloned image is a little more difficult than your important files – the size of the image being in the gigabytes means it will fill up a lot of cloud-storage services. If you have the space, definitely keep it on there; however, you may need to put it on an external hard drive.

Fig 1: Accessing the SD card from another PC is an easy alternative to transferring files between machines via a USB stick

Fig 2: Cloud storage services make backing up files easy and secure, as they're a lot less prone to problems

Fig 3: The dd tool is what you'll use on a Linux and Mac computer, and it's available by default in the terminal emulators

Fig 4: Win32 Disk Imager makes backing up the entire OS easy, and you can even use it to write the image back to the SD card

What you'll need…

Full nano manual
www.nano-editor.org/dist/v1.2/nano.1.html

Beginner's guide to nano

Learn how to edit text on the command line and in a terminal with one of Linux's best tools

Did you know…

Nano is one of the best command line editors for beginners, but there are lots of options like Kate and Vim.

If you have the itch to do more with your Pi, one of the skills you'll need to learn to pull off many projects is the ability to edit system files. The command line text editor nano is definitely one of the best tools for the job. Text editors are very basic tools; the clue is in the name in this case. There's no formatting or colouring or anything of the sort you would get in a word processor, but that's the point. The kind of files you'll be creating or editing will generally contain code – code which doesn't require to be made bold or bulleted. nano removes all of these distractions, but still has a few of the more handy features you'd find in a graphical text editor. We'll teach you how to make the most out of nano to make your projects run quickly and efficiently.

Writing
Create plain text files in the command line, even write some code for a program

Editing
Edit system files to suit your needs and projects without digging through a file manager

Advanced functions
Search, copy, paste and insert text from another file using some of the built-in nano functions

Open nano

01 Open the terminal, or enter the command line, and simply type **nano**. This will open a blank new file. From here you can create a simple text file such as a list, or create a system file, script or piece of code. How the system interprets your file depends on what you write and how you save it.

Save and continue

02 Once you've finished with nano, you can save/write out using Ctrl+O. All shortcuts and functions such as this are done using Ctrl and a letter key. It will ask you what name to save the file under. Whatever you name it, it will be saved in the directory you opened nano from unless you specify a path.

Opening files

03 To edit already existing files, you'll first need to know their location and name. To open them in nano, type the following:

```
$ nano /path/filename
```

For example, to edit fstab you would type:

```
$ nano /etc/fstab
```

Save and exit

04 Once you've finished modifying the file and need to get on with the next task, you can press Ctrl+X to exit nano. It will ask if you want to save any modifications, which just requires a Y to confirm. If you want to exit without saving changes, you can just use N. To cancel before making a decision, use Ctrl+C.

Copy and paste

05 This is more of a terminal-specific command, but it can be used just as well in nano. While you cannot use your mouse to navigate around the file in nano, you can highlight text in the same way you would in a graphical text editor. Once highlighted, pressing Ctrl+Shift+C will copy any text. Ctrl+Shift+V will paste.

Insert from file

06 If you need to directly insert the contents of another file, there's a quick way to do it without needing to use copy and paste. Typing Ctrl+R and entering the path to the file will insert it into the spot your cursor is at.

Advanced navigation

07 You've probably been using the arrow keys to move one space at a time left, right, up or down. There are other ways to move around the file, though. Using Ctrl+A will act the same way as the Home key does in a graphical editor, moving the cursor to the start of the line. Same with Ctrl+E moving you to the end like the End key. Ctrl+V is page down, and Ctrl+Y is page up.

Searching a file

08 Sometimes you'll be looking for a specific line or phrase in a large text file. Instead of using the arrow keys and tirelessly reading every line, you can use the search function via Ctrl+W. Entering the search term will begin looking through the document, and once you're finished you can press Ctrl+C to exit the search.

Extra help

09 There are many more functions available in nano. For a full list of commands, you can use Ctrl+G, which lists all the shortcuts and what they do. The caret symbol (^) in this list denotes the use of Ctrl on your keyboard.

What you'll need…

TightVNC
www.tightvnc.com/release-2.7.php

Did you know…

TightVNC Viewer is a free resource for accessing VNC servers, like the one we'll install in this tutorial.

Gain remote desktop access

Learn how to get access to your Raspberry Pi desktop without it being in front of you…

VNC (Virtual Network Computing) is a graphical desktop access and sharing system that allows a user to remotely control and use the desktop of another computer from their own system.

It's handy in many ways: to give you control over a remote system; to help out another user elsewhere; to allow a computer to remain powered on, but without the need for a keyboard, mouse or even a monitor.

In our case, we aim to allow access to the Raspberry Pi desktop without it being hooked up to the aforementioned peripherals. This way, you can do everything you would normally do, but with just the power supply and network attached, thereby freeing up space and saving extra expense. In real-world terms, this means you could potentially access the Pi desktop via an Android tablet or phone.

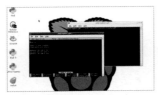

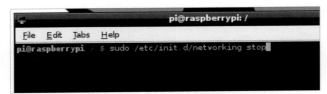

Static IP address

01 The first step for us is to make sure that the Raspberry Pi has a static IP address. Basically, an IP address is a group of numbers that your network assigns to devices in order to tell them apart. To set up a static IP address, simply double-click LXTerminal and type the following and then press Enter:

```
sudo nano /etc/network/
interfaces
```

Static IP part 2

02 This file controls the IP addressing for the Pi. You need to scroll down to the 'iface eth0' line and remove DHCP and replace it with static. Now, on the line directly below, enter the IP address that you want force your Pi to have, along with the subnet mask and the gateway:

```
address 192.168.1.93
netmask 255.255.255.0
gateway 192.168.1.254
```

Static IP part 3

03 After you've entered those details, exit nano by pressing Ctrl+X, followed by Y to accept the changes, and then press Enter a couple of times to get back to the command prompt in the terminal. You can now either reboot your Pi, or type the following into the terminal:

```
sudo /etc/init.d/networking stop
sudo /etc/init.d/networking
start
```

Installing VNC part 1

04 Now we'll install VNC and ensure that it starts automatically whenever the Pi is booted up. This used to be a bit annoying under older Raspbian versions, as configuring services often had a nasty habit of breaking the system. But no longer. Enter the following commands, pressing Enter after each one:

```
sudo apt-get update
sudo apt-get install tightvncserver
tightvncserver
```

Installing VNC part 2

05 When the packages have downloaded and installed, follow the instructions on screen (see below) to set up a password and confirm it, but answer 'n' to the view only option. This really is just a security feature and since you are only accessing the Pi at home, it's not absolutely necessary – it's still good practice, though.

```
You will require a password
  to access your
desktops
Password:
Verify:
Would you like to enter a
  view-only
password (y/n)? n
New 'X' desktop is raspberrypi:1
```

Configuring VNC server

06 That's the VNC server installed, up and running. Now we need to make sure it loads up as a service every time the Raspberry Pi reboots, so you can access it even if the Pi undergoes a power cycle. To configure the Pi to do this, type the following in the terminal and press Enter.

```
sudo nano /etc/init.d/
  tightvncserver
```

Configuring boot service

07 We're back in nano, and we'll need to enter some lines of commands in order to allow the Raspberry Pi to activate the VNC server when it boots. In the editor, type:

```
#!/bin/sh
# /etc/init.d/tightvncserver
# Set the VNCUSER variable to
the name of  the user to start
tightvncserver under
VNCUSER='pi'
case "$1" in
start)
su $VNCUSER -c '/usr/bin/
tightvncserver :1'
echo "Starting TightVNC
server for $VNCUSER"
;;
stop)
pkill Xtightvnc
echo "Tightvncserver stopped"
;;
*)
echo "Usage: /etc/init.d/
tightvncserver
{start|stop}"
exit 1
;;

esac
exit 0
```

Reboot and ready to go

08 Now press Ctrl+X, then Y to save, followed by Enter a couple of times to get you back into the Terminal. What we need to do now is edit the permissions of the script we've just created so that it's executable and active. Do this by typing the following commands into the terminal, ensuring that you press Enter after each one otherwise it will not be registered:

```
sudo chmod 755 /etc/init.d/
tightvncserver
update-rc.d tightvncserver
defaults
sudo reboot
```

Once you have completed these steps, the final thing that you will need to do is to unplug the Raspberry Pi and locate it somewhere that has easy access to a network cable. If you install the likes of TightVNC Viewer, or any other remote access software (as long as it uses the Tight protocol) then you should be able to point the client to the IP address 192.168.1.93:1 (or whatever the static IP address is of the network that you wish to connect the device to) and have full access to the Raspberry Pi.

What you'll need…

Any Raspberry Pi distro
www.raspberrypi.org/downloads

Internet connection

Second computer

Access your files with SSH

Use the terminal of your home computer to gain quick and secure access to your Raspberry Pi

While remotely logging into the full X environment is – as we demonstrated on the previous pages – very useful, it has its disadvantages. Firstly, it's not particularly quick or convenient to do. The user experience can be slow and cumbersome too, but worst of all, it's not as secure as we'd really like.

If you want to take a more convenient and secure approach to accessing your Raspberry Pi from another computer, you'll find that all well-versed Pi enthusiasts will use SSH. SSH stands for Secure Shell and is a cryptographic network protocol which is designed to ensure secure data communication via the command line. While beginners might argue it's easier to remotely access their Raspberry Pi using the full graphical interface, as soon as you've learnt a handful of basic command-line techniques you'll quickly find 'dipping in' to your Raspberry Pi via SSH is by far the most convenient way to talk to it remotely.

You'll be pleased to hear that SSH is already well configured out of the box – there's very little you need to do to make it work, especially if your remote computer runs Linux or OS X, as we're going to demonstrate here.

SSH is easy with Linux and OS X

Assuming your Raspberry Pi is on and connected to a network either by Ethernet or a Wi-Fi dongle, the only piece of information you need is the IP address of your Pi. To discover this, all you have to do is open a terminal window on your Raspberry Pi and type the command `ifconfig` (Fig 1).

If you're connected by Ethernet cable you'll see 'eth0', then several lines of results. The IP address will be the number on the second line next to words 'inet addr'. If you're connected by Wi-Fi,

Fig 1: Use the ifconfig command in the terminal to discover the IP address of your Raspberry Pi

the result will be on the second line of 'wlan0'. The IP address itself is a group of four numbers separated by full stops. If you're on your home network, it will likely be similar to 192.168.0.15. We'll use this number for our guide, but replace it with the IP address you've seen via ifconfig.

With this information in hand, all you need to do is open a terminal window on your remote Linux PC and type:

```
ssh pi@192.168.0.15
```

This assumes your Raspberry Pi's username is still the default (which is **pi**) and you're replacing the IP address with the one you made note of just now. If you've added user accounts or changed the default, you'll need to replace the username before the '@' with whatever you've changed it to. When you press Enter, you'll be prompted to enter the password for your Raspberry Pi – again, if it's the default you can type **raspberry**, otherwise type in your Pi's password and press Return.

You'll now see that the username details on the command line have changed to reflect those of your Raspberry Pi – you're now connected remotely. Try looking through your files or using nano to open a file to edit it!

Never type another IP address

Of course, if you take your Raspberry Pi to another network, your Pi's IP address will be different. If you just want to connect to it remotely, it becomes incredibly tiresome to set up your Pi with a keyboard, mouse and monitor just to get the IP address. Wouldn't it be easier if you could just type the Raspberry Pi's name into the terminal to connect? It sounds too good to be true, but it's actually very easy to do.

All you need is a small piece of software which effectively lets you discover hosts and services on your local network by name instead of IP address (Fig 2). To set it up on your Pi all you need to do is open a terminal and type:

```
sudo apt-get install avahi-daemon
```

Once the installation is complete, all you have to do to access your Raspberry Pi via SSH is type the following into the terminal:

```
ssh pi@raspberrypi.local
```

What's more, you can use the name of your Raspberry Pi when you access it via any other form of networking, be it Samba, remote login with VNC or anything else.

SSH with Windows

As is the way with most things in the Windows world, accessing your Raspberry Pi with Microsoft's operating system isn't quite as straightforward as you'd think. Fortunately, there is a useful tool to help. Putty allows you to make your Secure Shell connection and it's easy to set up and use. You can download Putty from: **www.chiark.greenend.org.uk/ ~sgtatham/putty**

Fig 2: The Avahi tool enables you to log into your Pi via SSH by name, rather than needing to discover its IP address

Raspberry Pi plus Arduinos

Find out just how to get your Raspberry Pi
to talk to and use your Arduino

The Raspberry Pi is a truly amazing single-board computer that gets used in lots of DIY projects. That has been the basis for this whole column and the previous several articles. While the Raspberry Pi has a GPIO and can communicate with sensors and actuators, you may have cases where you want to use your Raspberry Pi as the brains of your project and offload the interactions with the physical world to another system.

This is usually handled by one of the many microcontroller boards that are available. In this issue, we will specifically use the Arduino board and see how to connect it to a Raspberry Pi and how to handle the communications between the two. As always, we will be using Python as the language of choice to handle all of the actual coding in the examples here.

The Arduino is an open source prototyping platform defined as a specification. This means that you can get Arduino implementations from several different manufacturers, but they should all behave in a similar fashion. For this article, the assumption will be that whatever implementation you wish to use will behave properly. The first step is to connect the two boards together. You will probably want to use a powered USB hub to connect them since the Raspberry Pi can't provide huge amounts of power through its USB port. While they are connected over USB, the Arduino will appear as a serial port to the Raspberry Pi.

This means that you can communicate with the Arduino directly over the serial connection. To be completely sure you have all of the relevant libraries installed, you can simply install the Arduino IDE with the command:

```
sudo apt-get install arduino
```

This will make sure that you are starting with all of the core software that you might need. When you plug in your Arduino, you need to know over which port communications will happen. The specific port name will vary based on the exact version of Raspberry Pi and Arduino that you are using. However, it should be something like '/dev/ttyUSB0' or '/dev/ttyACM0'. In the example code below, we will be assuming that the Arduino is visible on the port '/dev/ttyUSB0'.

Once you have the two devices connected, you can start writing code to have them talk to

"For this article, the assumption will be that whatever implementation you wish to use will behave properly"

each other. We will start with the most low-level protocols and build upwards from there. The first step is to open a serial connection to the Arduino.

In order to do this, you will need to make sure that the Python serial module is installed. If you are using Raspbian, you can do this with:

```
sudo apt-get install python-serial
```

You then need to create a new Serial object connected to a given serial port, along with the speed you need to use.

```
import serial
ser = serial.Serial('/dev/ttyUSB0', 9600)
```

In the above example, the speed is 9600 baud (bits/sec). With this Serial object, you can read and write data to and from the Arduino. But you need code on the Arduino to handle its part of this communication. The Arduino has its own programming language, based on C, which you use to write the code that will run on the board. The way Arduinos work is that at bootup it will load a program that will run as long as it is powered up. As a simple example, the following code will listen on an input pin to see if it goes high. If so, it will then fire off a message on the serial port.

```
int pirPin = 7;
void setup() {
 pinMode(pirPin, INPUT);
 Serial.begin(9600);
}
void loop() {
 if (digitalRead(pirPin) == HIGH) {
   Serial.println("High");
 }
   delay(500);
 }
```

To load this program to your Arduino board, you will need to use the Arduino IDE that was installed at the beginning of this article. This is a graphical program, so you will need to connect your Raspberry Pi to a monitor if you want to do this step using it. Otherwise, you can do this programming of your Arduino using your regular desktop. If you are using the standard bootloader on most Arduinos, it will start up whatever program was last uploaded to it. This way you can use your desktop to upload your code and then connect it to your Raspberry Pi later on. Moving back to the Raspberry Pi, how can you read this message from the Arduino? You can simply do a read from the Serial object that you created earlier.

```
import time
while True:
  message = ser.readline()
  print(message)
  if (message[0] == 'H')
    do_something_useful()
  time.sleep(.5)
```

As you can see, we imported the time module in order to be able to sleep in the loop between attempts to read from the serial port. What about sending instructions out to the Arduino? This is also requires Arduino code to be uploaded ahead of time. For example, the following code will take an input number andflash an LED that number of times

```
int ledPin = 13;
void setup() {
  pinMode(ledPin, OUPUT);
  Serial.begin(9600);
}
void loop() {
if (Serial.available()) {
  flash(Serial.read() - '0');
}
```

```
delay(1000);
}
void flash(int n) {
for (int i = 0; i < n; i++) {
  digitalWrite(ledPin, HIGH);
    delay(100);
    digitalWrite(ledPin, LOW);
    delay(100);
  }
}
```

Then, you can send a count from your Python code with something like:

```
ser.write('5')
```

This will flash the LED 5 connected to pin 13 on your Arduino five times. One missing element on the Raspberry Pi is an analogue-to-digital (ADC) converter to take a given voltage and turn it into a number that can be used in some piece of control software. This is where attaching an Arduino can be extremely helpful, as it has a 10-bit ADC converter included. The following code will read the voltage on pin 3 and then send it out over the serial connection to the Raspberry Pi.

```
int analogPin = 3;
int val = 0;
void setup() {
Serial.begin(9600);
}
void loop() {
val = analogRead(analogPin);
Serial.println(val);
}
```

This maps the measured voltage to an integer between 0 and 1,023. The minimum voltage is zero, while the maximum voltage can be set with the function analogReference(). By default, the maximum is the power supplied to the board (5 volts for 5V boards, or 3.3 volts for 3.3V boards). You can also use two internally supplied reference voltages, one at 1.1 volts and a second at 2.56 volts. For special cases, you can supply an external reference voltage to the AREF pin. You need to be sure that it is only between 0 volts and 5 volts.

Going in the opposite direction, you can use the Arduino to supply an output voltage. This is done by using a PWM (pulse width modulation) output signal. The idea is to actually send out a number of pulses with some duty cycle that is on for some percentage of the time and off for the remainder of the time. For example, if you have an LED connected to one of the pins, you can light it at half brightness with the following code.

```
int ledPin = 9;
void setup() {
pinMode(ledPin, OUTPUT);
}
void loop() {
analogWrite(ledPin, 127);
}
```

The second parameter to the analogWrite() function is a value between 0 and 255, which defines the duty cycle between 0% (or fully off) to 100% (or fully on). This analog output signal stays on at the given duty cycle until a new call to the analogWrite() function. By having your Raspberry Pi write out values over the serial connection, it can then control the output duty cycle by sending a simple integer. This short article will spark some ideas on how you can start combining multiple computing platforms to expand the capabilities of your own projects.

There is no reason to try to find the one silver-bullet platform for your project when you can pick the sub-modules that actually do their own individual jobs best and build up the complex behaviour you need from these simpler parts.

PyFirmata can help even more

Discover ways to make interacting easier

While you can write your own code to run on the Arduino, there are several projects that can be uploaded to it to make interacting a bit easier. One of these is the Firmata project, which includes a Python module to help you talk to the Arduino. The first step will be downloading the Firmata Arduino code and uploading it to your Arduino, most easily done with a desktop computer. The code is available at github.com/firmata/arduino. There are a few different versions available, but for these examples you should upload the StandardFirmata sketch with the Arduino IDE. There are client libraries available for many different programming languages, including several for Python. The one we will look at using is pyFirmata. You can install it on your Raspberry Pi with:

```
sudo pip install pyFirmata
```

You can now use Firmata to act as a sort of remote control to the Arduino port, where your Python code can get almost direct access to all of the functionality available. To get started, import the pyFirmata module and create a new Arduino object connected to the relevant serial port:

```
import pyfirmata
board = pyfirmata.Arduino('/dev/ttyUSB0')
```

You can now access digital I/O pins directly. For example, the following code would write a 1 to pin 10.

```
board.digital[10].write(1)
```

When you want to read from a pin, you have the possibility of overflowing input buffers. To deal with this issue, you can create an iterator object and start it before doing any reads, using code like that below.

```
it = pyfirmata.util.Iterator(board)
it.start()
```

You can now get selected pins for either input or output. The following code will get pin 4 for digital input and pin 12 for analogue PWM output.

```
pin4 = board.get_pin('d:4:i')
pin12 = board.get_pin('a:12:p')
```

You can then read and write with these new pin objects with the related methods:

```
val = pin4.read()
pin12.write(100)
```

When you are done, don't forget to reset any output pins back to 0 volts, and then you can close down the connection with:

```
board.exit()
```

"There are a few different versions available, but for these examples you should upload StandardFirmata sketch with the Arduino IDE"

What you'll need...

Scratch
Internet connection

Program with Scratch

An interactive guide to coding with the Pi's graphical programming language

Would you like to delve into the world of animation and game creation? Do you want to bring your creative ideas to life without learning a software-development language? With Scratch you can do all this, and much more.

Scratch 1.4 is already installed on the official 'wheezy' Raspbian operating system image. If your Raspberry Pi doesn't already have Scratch installed, don't worry, just hop on over to the official MIT Scratch website to find the download and install instructions.

To begin, all we need to do is open the Scratch Studio. Click on Scratch's cat icon on the desktop, or find Scratch in the LXDE desktop menu.

The Scratch Studio is a complete development environment. It's divided up into a number of separate panels. Each panel has a specific role in the app-construction process and its own specific set of features and tools.

Scratch studio projects

01 Located at the top of the Studio are three quick-access icons and the main menu (Fig 2).

The first globe-style icon sets the language for the Studio. The other two buttons provide rapid access to the project save and share features.

Under the 'File' menu there's a typical set of file-management features to open, save and import Scratch projects. There is also a 'Project Notes' option where we are able to enter feature descriptions and comments.

The 'Edit' menu contains a mixed bag of animation, image and audio-editing tools. While the 'Help' section

provides access to the browser-hosted help pages.

Rather interestingly, the 'Share' menu allows us to share our projects with the whole world. Any Scratch project can be posted onto the Scratch community website via the 'Share This Project Online...' option

and the 'Upload To Scratch Server' form (Fig 3).

Let's load the 'Aquarium' example project. Select the 'Open...' option in the 'File' menu to display the Open Project dialogue. From the list of large buttons on the left, click on the one called 'Examples'. Next, on the right, select the 'Animation' folder with a double click. Then select the '6 Aquarium' item. The open dialogue window contents should look like the one in Fig 4.

With the Aquarium project loaded our Scratch Studio should look similar to Fig 1. We'll begin our Studio tour with the staging area.

Fig 3: Project Share Dialogue – We can share our projects using the Studio's Share menu

Fig 2: Scratch Studio Menu – Scratch Studio's main menu and shortcut icons in action

Fig 4: File Open Dialogue – Use the Studio's File menu and 'Open…' to load the Aquarium project

Scratch studio stage

02 The stage is where all the action takes place and is located at the upper right of the Scratch Studio.

The stage is constructed from graphical elements called sprites. Here we have plants, bubbles, fish and other creatures. You can also add and create your own assets with scratch, but we'll come to that later.

At the top of the 'Staging Area' there's a green flag and a red circle. Click on the green flag to bring the aquarium to life. Now spend a little time studying the Aquarium animation. Note the creature's movements and rising bubbles. The red circle icon stops the action.

We can set the view mode with the three buttons located just above the green flag.

The two left-hand buttons increase or decrease the size of the Staging Area panel. A smaller Staging Area means the central area of the Studio increases in relative size compared.

The right-hand button is the Presentation Mode which displays the stage in full-screen mode (see Fig 5). Exit presentation mode with the curly arrow button at the top left, or press the 'esc' key.

Scratch studio sprites

03 Beneath the Staging Area is the collection of sprites for this project. The 'Stage' sprite is separated from the rest. It's a little different to the others and acts as the background image for the stage.

The three buttons across the top of this area offer various ways to create a new sprite. The first button opens up a blank canvas in the Paint Editor. The second button creates a new sprite based in an image file, as selected by the popup file section dialogue window. The third will select a random image from the pre-installed image collection.

We can manage sprites directly from the stage using the four buttons to the right of the main menu. Here we click on a particular button and then a sprite on the stage.

Fig 5: Stage Presentation Mode – The Studio's stage presentation mode is the best way to see the project

Use Scratch blocks and tools

Getting to grips with the Scratch Studio toolbox

Situated in the centre of the Studio is the Edit Panel. The panel contents relate to the currently selected sprite.

Let's start by selecting the jelly fish sprite, called Creature1, from the Sprite Collection area.

At the top we have the sprite's image and name, plus an indication of its current stage coordinates and direction. On the left are three animation control buttons. The top button will rotate the sprite, the second switches between left- and right-facing states, and the third turns animation off.

Below are three Edit Panel tabs. The script tab is where block scripts are created. Here's where we'll drag and drop our blocks, snapping them together in various combinations.

To change a sprite's visual appearance we'll use the 'Costumes' tab. Each sprite can have one or more costumes. For example, the jellyfish has two costumes (Fig 1). Each costume has buttons to edit, copy and delete. New costumes can be painted, imported or captured using the three 'New Costumes' buttons. The sound tab allows us to add audio to our project.

Fig 1: Jellyfish Sprite Costumes – The jellyfish sprite has two different costumes

Scratch block styles

01 The 'Blocks Palette' contains the complete collection of scripting blocks. Blocks come in three basic styles, namely hats, stacks and reporters (see Fig 3 on the opposite page).

A hat-style block will start block script execution based on a specific event. The classic hat block is the 'green flag' click event. However, there are numerous other hat blocks, including hat blocks that start script execution after a specific key press, a mouse click and even following sensor event from the some GPIO connected hardware. As you can probably tell, this offers a lot of options to Scratch programmers.

Reporter blocks allow us to specify textual, numeric and boolean values. They fit into specific shaped 'holes' in other blocks. A rectangular reporter will contain a text string. While the rounded end reporters are associated with numeric values, angle-ended reporters contain boolean true and false values.

Stack blocks are the core script building elements. They interconnect with other blocks via their top-edge notches and bottom-edge bumps. Many stack blocks contain 'holes' for reporter style blocks, which will modify their operation depending on the specified reporter block values.

The Scratch block collection is divided into groups. We select a block group using the eight buttons located at the top of the Block Palette panel, namely 'Motion', 'Control', 'Looks' and so on. These groups are colour coded. Apart from aiding block selection this colour coding provides a visual clue to a block's type when reading a block script in the Edit Panel.

Fig 2: Sound Recorder Tool – Scratch Studio includes a tool to record our own sounds

Scratch block help

02 As we've seen, there are many blocks, each with their own specific functionality and capabilities.

In one way this is great news. A large block collection means Scratch can be used in a vast range of software projects, such as games, animation, music, graphics, math, science, robotics, electronics and much more.

However, the wide selection of blocks can be quite a challenge for the novice Scratch coder. To help with this problem the Scratch Studio designers have included an informative set of block-centric help pages.

A simple right click on any block will display a pop-up help page option. The help page contains context-specific descriptions, graphical images and, where appropriate, a script example of how to use this particular block (Fig 4).

It's a terrific feature which greatly simplifies the process of deciding which blocks to use. More importantly, studying these help pages is a highly effective way to enhance our scripting skills and discover the potential contained within Scratch's feature-rich block collection.

Block script walkthrough

03 Let's dig deeper into how a block script works in practice. For this, we will use a simple Aquarium project block script. From the 'Sprite Collection' panel select the Stage sprite. Then go back to the central 'Edit Panel' and select the 'Scripts' tab.

There's just a single block script. Starting at the top there's a 'green flag' hat-style block to kick off the activity. Next there's a 'forever loop'. The blocks inside this loop are actioned until the stop button is pressed. This forever loop block contains two other blocks.

The first inner script block selects the next background image. Click on the 'Backgrounds' tab to view all the stage images. The second inner block simply pauses execution for a number of seconds. Setting the value to '1' means that this script will pause for a second before then performing the action specified by the next block.

It's important that you remember these two blocks are enclosed in the forever loop block. So, the stage background images will be displayed in sequence for one second each.

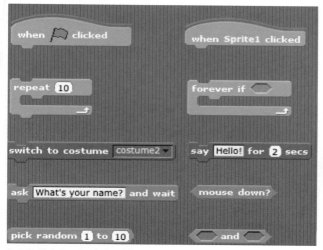

Fig 3: Block Style Examples – the Scratch blocks come in a number of different styles

Fig 4: Block Help Window – Example of the help window associated with an 'ask and wait' block

What you'll need…

Scratch project archives
www.scratch.mit.edu/explore/?date=ever

Create a Snake clone in Scratch

Design your own version of Snake to test your new programming skills!

Here, we will create a version of the classic Snake game where you move the snake around the Scratch stage using the arrow keys. You control the head of the snake and must avoid a collision with either the body of the snake or the edge of the stage.

The snake body grows longer each time you eat an egg. You get points added to your score for eating good yellow eggs and lose points for eating bad black eggs. There are also bonus sprites to eat for extra points.

By following this tutorial you will learn to create your own simple sprite graphics, send and receive broadcast events, use a list variable to store data, play sound effects, generate random numbers and use sensing commands to detect when a sprite is touching something.

Egg sprite
The Egg sprite appears randomly on the screen and lets other sprites know when it has been eaten (touched by the snake tongue)

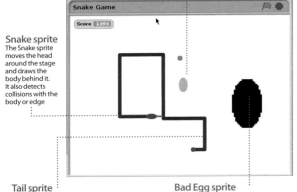

Snake sprite
The Snake sprite moves the head around the stage and draws the body behind it. It also detects collisions with the body or edge

Tail sprite
The Tail sprite follows the head, erasing the end of the body so the snake moves, and pausing when it needs to grow

Bad Egg sprite
The Bad Egg sprite also appears randomly but decreases the score when eaten. It also grows in size, getting harder to avoid

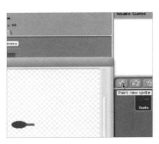

Paint the Snake sprite

01 Click the New Sprite: Paintbrush icon to paint the Snake sprite. In the Paint Editor, draw a small green ellipse for the snake head and add a red rectangle for the tongue. It's important that the tongue is a different colour to the head. Name your sprite Snake.

Add a Snake sound

02 When the Snake tongue touches the snake body or the edge of the stage, we are going to play a Game Over sound. We need to add this sound to the Snake sprite. With the Snake sprite selected, click the Sound tab and choose Import. Select the Electronic>Screech sound.

Respond to arrow keys

03 Drag four when key pressed commands from the Control palette, and four point in direction commands from the Motion palette. Configure them as shown so that the up arrow changes the direction to 0 degrees (up) and so on. Click the green flag above the stage to test this.

Make Snake variables

04 Click on the Variables palette. Make two variables, Score and Speed, that are visible to all sprites. Make a list called Next Direction which is visible to all sprites; it will store the sequence of directions that the head takes. Only have the Score variable checked so it appears on the stage.

Initialise Snake variables

05 Use a 'when green flag clicked' Control command and initialise the Snake variables as shown, using commands from the Variables palette. We want to start each game with an empty Next Direction list, so delete all of its entries. The Score must start at zero. The Speed sets difficulty.

Draw Snake body

06 Use commands from the Pen palette to control the drawing of the snake body. You should also use commands from the Motion palette to move the snake to the centre of the stage and point left at the beginning of each game. The pen is up until the snake is in the starting position. In the next steps we'll use colours to check to see if the head is touching anything it shouldn't.

Add main action loop

07 Use a 'forever' command with an 'if-else' command nested inside. We have a collision if the red tongue is touching the blue body (the head is always touching the body) or the Snake sprite is touching the edge. Use the Eyedropper tool to select colours within Scratch.

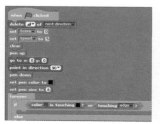

Handle Game Over

08 When a collision has been detected, broadcast a Game Over event (you'll need to create a new event) to the other sprites so they can also react. Also, play the Screech sound effect and stop all scripts so that the snake freezes in its current position at the end of the game.

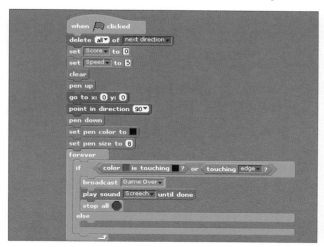

Handle movement

09 Now handle the typical case where there is no collision and the snake must move in its current direction. The pen is down so it will draw the body. The Speed variable determines how many steps to move. Add the current direction to the Next Direction list for the tail to read.

Try out the snake

10 You can now try out your Snake sprite. It will move around the screen in response to pressing the arrow keys. It will draw its body, which will just get longer and longer because we need the tail to erase it. And it will screech and end the game on detecting a collision.

Paint the tail

11 Click the New Sprite: Paintbrush icon to paint the Tail sprite. Draw a small green circle to represent the end of the tail. Name this sprite Tail. The Tail sprite will follow the Snake and erase the end of its tail so that the snake body doesn't grow indefinitely.

Make a Grow variable

12 Make a Grow variable which is for this sprite only – no other sprites need access to it. The Grow variable is used to determine when the snake body needs to grow and the tail therefore needs to pause before following to allow the head to get further ahead.

Handle events

13 The Tail needs to listen for two new events which you create as you need them. When it receives an Egg Eaten event from one of the Egg sprites, it sets Grow=1 so that the tail can pause. And when it receives a Game Over event from the Snake, it must freeze.

Initialise the tail

14 When the green flag is clicked to start the game, Grow is set to 1 so the snake gets a short body. Move to the centre of the stage with the pen up and configure the pen to draw a trail the same colour and size as the stage background so that it erases the body.

Grow and move

15 Use a 'forever' command to keep the tail moving. If Grow is 1 it should pause and reset Grow to 0 – this makes the body grow longer. Use the first value from Next Direction to set the direction and remove it so you get a new value next time. Move Speed steps.

Try out the tail

16 Now you can try out the Tail sprite. The snake won't keep growing yet because it won't receive any Egg Eaten events. But the tail will follow the snake head around the stage, erasing the snake body as it goes by drawing over it with a white pen (which is the same colour as the background).

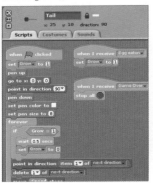

Paint the Egg sprite

17 Click the New Sprite: Paintbrush icon to paint a new sprite. In the Paint Editor, draw a small yellow ellipse. Name the sprite Egg. The Egg will appear randomly on the stage and cause the snake to grow and increase its score.

Add Egg sound

18 Go to the Sounds tab for the Egg sprite and import the Percussion>Cymbal Crash sound. Or you can choose a different sound if you like. This sound will play when the snake eats an egg.

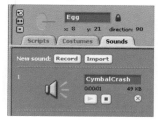

Add Egg scripts

19 Copy the Egg script so that the Egg appears randomly at the start of the game. When the Egg senses that it has been eaten, it must hide, play the Cymbal sound (or whatever you chose in Step 18), update the score, broadcast the Egg Eaten event and then randomly appear again. When the Game Over event is received, it must stop.

Make Bad Egg

20 Create the black Bad Egg in the same way as the Egg but using a different graphic and the Instruments>StringPluck sound. Drag the Egg's green flag scripts onto the Bad Egg to copy them – just change the sound that's played and reduce the score instead of increasing it.

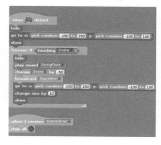

Grow Bad Egg

21 Add another 'when green flag clicked' script to the Bad Egg so it sets its size to the default 100% when a new game is started and then increases its size by ten every ten seconds. The Bad Egg will get bigger and bigger and harder to avoid.

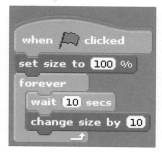

Create Bonus sprite

22 Create the Bonus sprite in a similar way. You can choose the shape and sound for the Bonus. Its scripts are similar to the Egg ones so you could drag one of those to the Bonus sprite and work from that. Make sure you change the sound and increase the score by a random bonus.

Check your mail

With Python, you can have your Raspberry Pi act as mail checker, giving you a running list on incoming email

Since the Raspberry Pi is such a small computer, it gets used in a lot of projects where you want to monitor a source of data. One such monitor you might want to create is a mail-checker that can display your current unread emails. This issue, we'll look at how to use Python to create your own mail-checking monitor to run on your Pi. We'll focus on the communications between the Pi and the mail server and not worry too much about how it might be displayed. That will be left as a further exercise.

To start with, most email servers use one of two different communication protocols. The older, simpler one was called POP (Post Office Protocol), and the newer one is called IMAP (Internet Message Access Protocol). We will cover both protocols to cover all of the situations that you might run into. We'll start with the older POP communications protocol. Luckily, there is support for this protocol as part of the standard library. In order to start using this protocol, you will need to import the poplib module, and then create a new POP3 object. For example, the following will create a connection to the POP server available through Gmail.

```
import poplib
my_pop = poplib.POP3_SSL(host='pop.gmail.com')
```

You need to use the POP3_SSL class when connecting to Gmail because Google uses SSL for its connections. If connecting to a different email server, you can use POP3 to make an unencrypted connection. The POP communication protocol involves the client sending a series of commands to the server to interact with it. For example, you can get the welcome message from the server with the getwelcome() method:

```
my_pop.getwelcome()
```

The first things that you will want to communicate to the server are the username and password for an email account that you are interested in. Having the username in your code is not too much of a security issue, but the password is another matter. Unless you have a good reason to have it written out in your code, you should probably ask the end-user for it. Included within the standard library is the getpass module, which you can use to ask the end-user for their password in a safer fashion. You could use the following code, for example.

```
import getpass
my_pop.user('my_name@gmail.com')
my_pop.pass_(getpass.getpass())
```

"The first things that you will want to communicate to the server are the username and password for an email account"

You should now be fully logged in to your email account. Under POP, your account will be locked until you choose to execute the quit() method of the connection. If you need a quick summary of what is on the open server you can execute the stat() method:

```
my_pop.stat()
```

This method returns a tuple consisting of the message count and the mailbox size. You can get an explicit list of messages with the list() method. You have two options for looking at the actual contents of these emails, depending on whether you want to leave the messages untouched or not. If you want to simply look at the first chunk of the messages, you can use the top() method. The following code will grab the headers and the first five lines of the first message in the list.

```
email_top = my_pop.top(1, 5)
```

This method will return a tuple consisting of the response text from the email server, a list of the headers and the number of requested lines, and the octet count for the message. The one problem with the top() method is that it is not always well implemented on every email server. In those cases, you can use the retr() method. It will return the entire requested message in the same form as that returned from top().

Once you have your message contents, you need to decide what you actually want to display. As an example, you might want to simply print out the subject lines for each message. You could do that with the following code.

```
for line in email_top[1]:
if 'Subject' in i:
```

```
print(i)
```

You need to explicitly do the search because the number of lines included in the headers varies between each message. Once you're done, don't forget to execute the quit() method to close down your connection to the email server. One last thing to consider is how long the email server will keep the connection alive. While running test code for this article, it would frequently time out. If you need to, you can use the noop() method as a keep-alive for the connection.

As mentioned previously, the second, newer, protocol for talking to email servers is IMAP. Luckily, there is a module included in the standard library that you can use, similar to the poplib module we looked at above, called imaplib. Also, as above, it contains two main classes to encapsulate the connection details. If you need an SSL connection, you can use IMAP4_SSL. Otherwise, you can use IMAP4 for unencrypted connections. Using Gmail as an example, you can create an SSL connection with the following code.

```
import imaplib
import getpass
my_imap = imaplib.IMAP4_SSL('imap.gmail.com')
```

As opposed to poplib, imaplib has a single method to handle authentication. You can use the getpass module to ask for the password.

```
my_imap.login('my_username@gmail.com', getpass.getpass())
```

IMAP contains the concept of a tree of mailboxes where all of your emails are organised. Before you can start to look at the emails, you need to select which mailbox you want to work with. If you don't give a mailbox name, the default is the inbox.

This is fine since we only want to display the newest emails which have come in. Most of the interaction methods return a tuple that contains a status flag (either 'OK' or 'NO') and a list containing the actual data. The first thing we need to do after selecting the inbox is to search for all of the messages available, as in the following example.

```
my_imap.select()
typ, email_list = my_imap.search(None, 'ALL')
```

The email_list variable contains a list of binary strings that you can use to fetch individual messages. You should check the value stored in the variable typ to be sure that it contains 'OK'. To loop through the list and select a given email, you can use the following code:

```
for num in email_list[0].split():
    typ, email_raw = my_imap.fetch(num, '(RFC822)')
```

The variable email_raw contains the entire email body as a single escaped string. While you could parse it to pull out the pieces that you want to display in your email monitor, that kind of defeats the power of Python.

Again, available in the standard library is a module called email that can handle all of those parsing issues. You will need to import the module in order to use it, as in the example here.

```
import email
email_mesg = email.message_from_bytes(email_
raw[0][1])
```

All of the sections of your email are now broken down into sections that you can pull out much more easily. Again, to pull out the subject line for a quick display, you can use the code:

```
subject_line = email_mesg.get('Subject')
```

There are many different potential items that you could select out. To get the full list of available header items, you can use the keys method, as shown below:

```
email_mesg.keys()
```

Many times, the emails you get will come as multi-part messages. In these cases, you will need to use the get_payload() method to extract any attached parts. It will come back as a list of further email objects. You then need to use the get_payload() method on those returned email objects to get the main body. The code might look like:

```
payload1 = email_mesg.get_payload()[0]
body1 = payload1.get_payload(
```

As with POP email connections, you may need to do something to keep the connection from timing out. If you do, you can use the noop() method of the IMAP connection object. This method acts as a keep-alive function.

When you are all done, you need to be sure to clean up after yourself before shutting down. The correct way to do this is to close the mailbox you have been using first, and then log out from the server. An example is given here:

```
my_imap.logout()
my_imap.close()
```

You now should have enough information to be able to connect to an email server, get a list of messages, and then pull out the sections that you might want to display as part of your email monitor. For example, if you are displaying the information on an LCD, you might just want to have the subject lines scrolling past. If you are using a larger screen display, you might want to grab a section of the body, or the date and time, to include as part of the information.

"When you are done, you need to be sure to clean up after yourself before shutting down"

What about sending emails?

Find out how to send as well as receive

In the main body of the article, we have only looked at how to connect to an email server and how to read from it. But what if you need to be able to also send emails off using some code? Similar to poplib and imaplib, the Python standard library includes a module called smtplib. Again, similar to poplib and imaplib, you need to create an SMTP object for the connection, and then log in to the server. If you are using the GMail SMTP server, you could use the code

```
import smtplib
import getpass
my_smtp = smtplib.SMTP_SSL('smtp.gmail.com')
my_smtp.login('my_email@gmail.com', getpass.
getpass())
```

This code asks the end user for their password, but if you aren't concerned about security, you could have it hard-coded into the code. Also, you only need to use the login() method for those servers that require it. If you are running your own SMTP server, you may have it set up to accept unauthenticated connections. Once you are connected and authenticated, you can now send emails out. The main method to do this is called

sendmail(). As an example, the following code sends a 'Hello World' email to a couple of people.

```
my_smtp.sendmail('my_email@gmail.com',
['friend1@email.com', 'friend2@email.com'], 'This
email\r\nsays\r\nHello World')
```

The first parameter is the 'from' email address. The second parameter is a list of 'to' email addresses. If you have only a single 'to' address, you can put it as a single string rather than a list. The last parameter is a string containing the body of the email you are trying to send. One thing to be aware of is that you will only get an exception if the email can't be sent to any of the 'to' email addresses specified.

As long as the message can be sent to at least one of the given addresses, it will return as completed. Once you have finished sending your emails, you can clean up with the code:

```
my_smtp.quit()
```

This cleans everything up and shuts down all active connections. So now your project can reply to incoming emails, too.

What you'll need…

Raspbian
www.raspberrypi.org/downloads

SD card

Supercharge your Pi

Get the most out of your Raspberry Pi with these performance-enhancing tips and tricks

Your Raspberry Pi is plugged in. Raspbian is installed on the SD card and you are right in the middle of setting up a wireless print server or building a robot to collect your mail from your doormat. But are you truly getting the most from your little computer? Perhaps you haven't explored the full set of options in Raspbian, or you're running the entire OS from SD card, something that can reduce SD card lifespan. Various tools and techniques can be employed to improve performance, from choosing the right hardware to overclocking the CPU. You might even maximise storage space on the Pi's SD card or all but replace it with a secondary device. Use these tips and tricks to reconfigure your Pi setup and optimise software and hardware to ensure you get the best performance.

Use better storage hardware

01 Your choice of storage media can have an impact on your Raspberry Pi's performance, regardless of the operating system. A low capacity SD card with poor error correction, is going to be slower than a larger card with greater resilience, so you need to find the right balance for your project and shop wisely.

Choosing the best SD card

02 Various standards of SD card are available, with the more expensive designed for better error correction. For the best performance on your Raspberry Pi, choose an SDHC card with a high rating. The same advice applies to MicroSD cards, which you can use on your Raspberry Pi with an SD card adaptor or directly insert into a Raspberry Pi B+.

Make the most of your storage

03 You'll typically need 1-2GB of storage for your chosen Raspberry Pi distro, so any remaining storage on your SD card will be used for updates and data you create or save. In Raspbian you can open a command line and run the configuration utility to gain more space (only if your SD card's greater than 2GB):

```
sudo raspi-config
```

Expand the Raspbian partition

04 Maximising the partition affords the full capacity of your SD card, which will increase the media's lifespan (there is more space to write too, so the same sectors aren't being overwritten as often). With raspi-config running, use the arrow keys to select expand_rootfs in the menu. Then wait briefly while the partition is resized.

Write data to RAM

05 Rather than reading and writing data to your SD card – something that will eventually result in a deterioration of reliability and performance in the card – you can configure Raspbian to write to the system RAM, which will speed things up slightly and improve the SD card's overall performance. This is achieved using fstab (file systems table), a system configuration available in most Linux distros.

Enable fstab in Raspbian

06 This is much like creating a RAM disk in Windows. In the command line, enter:

```
sudo nano /etc/fstab
```
Add the following line to mount a virtual file system:
```
tmpfs /var/log tmpfs
    defaults,noatime,nosuid,mode=
    0755,size=100m 0 0
```
Follow this by saving and exiting nano (Ctrl+X), then safely restarting the Pi:
```
sudo shutdown -r now
```

"You'll typically need 1-2GB of storage for your chosen Raspberry Pi distro"

Picking an external USB drive

Speeding up your Raspberry Pi by migrating the root filesystem to an external USB drive is a start, but what sort of device should you use for the best performance? With a USB thumb drive you can add flash storage up to 16GB without running into any significant problems (the larger the drive, the greater the current is required to read/write). Anything larger is expensive and unnecessary. If you're planning to use an external HDD, there are no power issues as it will have its own power supply. As ever, your choice should suit your project.

Below Having your filesystem on a USB stick is great for backups as well as performance boosts

Supercharge your Pi

Configure fstab for fast performance

07 Upon restarting, the virtual filesystem will be mounted and /var/log on the RAM disk. Other directories that can be moved to RAM include:

```
tmpfs /tmp tmpfs defaults,noatime,nosuid,size=100m 0 0
tmpfs /var/tmp tmpfs defaults,noatime,nosuid,size=30m 0 0
tmpfs /var/log tmpfs defaults,noatime,nosuid,mode=0755,size=100m 0 0
tmpfs /var/run tmpfs defaults,noatime,nosuid,mode=0755,size=2m 0 0
tmpfs /var/spool/mqueue tmpfs defaults,noatime,nosuid,mode=0700,gid=
  12,size=30m 0 0
```
Add each to /etc/fstab in nano.

Move your OS to a HDD

08 If you're concerned about the lifespan of the SD card, why not reduce your Raspberry Pi's reliance on it? Instead of using the SD card as a sort of budget SSD, change its role and add a HDD or USB stick to run the operating system, leaving the SD card for bootstrapping. This can give a marked performance boost to the SD card.

Back up the SD card

09 Create a copy of your Pi's SD card. Shut down, remove the card and insert it into your desktop computer. In the command line, run:

```
sudo dd bs=4M if=/dev/sdb of=~/backup.img
```
The path /dev/sdb represents the SD card. Copying takes 5-10 minutes. When complete, remove the SD card and connect your USB device.

Copy Raspbian to USB

10 Using a blank Ext4-formatted USB thumb drive (or external HDD) as the destination drive, enter:

```
sudo dd bs=4M if=~/backup.img of=/dev/sdc
```
Leave the backup on your computer, just in case something goes wrong. With an SD card and USB storage device sharing an identical disk image, it's time to consider what you're going to do next – create a faster Raspberry Pi.

Split the Raspbian partitions

11 Ideally, the boot partition should remain on the SD card while the root filesystem is run from the external HDD or USB thumb drive. Using your preferred partition manager (Disk Utility is in most distros), unmount and delete the root filesystem from the SD card, ensuring you have retained the boot partition. After removing the SD card, connect your USB device and delete the boot partition, taking care to leave the root filesystem intact. Then resize the root filesystem on the USB device, making sure that 10MB remains.

Identify the root filesystem

12 You're going to have the SD card and the external USB storage connected, so you need to tell the Pi where the root filesystem is. On the desktop Linux computer with your SD card inserted, run:

    sudo nano /boot/cmdline.txt

Find root=/dev/mmcblk0p2 (or similar) and change that to read root=/dev/sda2 which is your external USB storage. Save and exit.

Add other USB devices

13 You can now restart your Pi with the storage devices attached, but as soon as you connect further USB media you'll suffer problems. Avoid by installing gdisk:

    sudo apt-get update
    sudo apt-get install gdisk

Then run gdisk:

    sudo gdisk /dev/sdb

Enter ? to display the options and select Recovery and Transformation options (experts only), followed by Load MBR and Build Fresh GPT. Tap ? one last time and select 'Write Table to Disk' and exit. Remove and replace the USB device and run gdisk again. This time enter I and then 1 to display the Partition Unique GUID.

Above Heat sinks for the Pi are widely available and usually cost less than $10

Make your Pi fast and reliable

14 Make a note of the GUID and then switch to the SD card. Reopen cmdline. txt and change root=/dev/mmcblk0p2 to root=PARTUUID=XXXXXX, where the numerical string from the partition unique GUID should replace the XXXXXX. When you're done, save and exit. You can then start your Raspberry Pi. Congratulations, your Raspberry Pi is now faster and more reliable to use.

Boost performance with overclocking

15 Need more from your Pi? It is possible to overclock the computer, although you should be aware of the risks inherent with this activity. You should also ensure that your Raspberry Pi's processor is suitably cooled – heatsinks for the CPU, Ethernet controller and power regulator can be purchased online.

Overclock your Pi

16 Overclocking is available through raspi-config. Launch from the command line and arrow down to the overclock option. Four further options are available: Modest, Medium, High and Turbo. With your ideal clock speed selected, exit raspi-config and restart your Raspberry Pi to apply:

    sudo shutdown -r now

Now you will need to perform tests to see how stable it is overclocked. Raspberry Pi founder, Eben Upton, suggests running Quake 3 as a good stress test. Should the Pi fail to boot, hold Shift to boot without overclocking, run raspi-config and select a more modest overclock.

Run Raspbian without the GUI

17 Despite these changes, you may find that the GUI remains slow. If you find yourself running a lot of commands in bash, the best thing to do is disable launching into X. In raspi-config, choose boot_behaviour and select the first (default) option to ensure your Pi boots to the command line. Should you need the GUI, enter 'startx' in Terminal.

What you'll need…

NagiosPi
piimagehub.com/project/nagiospi

Win32 Disk Imager
bit.ly/L8JdYG

Disk Utility
bit.ly/1Lec9r5

Internet connection

4 GB (or larger) SD card

Monitor your local network with NagiosPi

Embrace the power of Nagios to keep an eye on servers, switches and applications on your network

Is your PC offline? Has your Linux box stopped serving Minecraft or Counter-Strike? If you're out of the house, or even the country, there is no real way of knowing without trying to log in – something you probably won't be able to do without being on the premises (unless you're using remote desktop software).

A far better way would be to simply receive notifications when your network devices are knocked offline, and this is why we turn to NagiosPi, a Raspberry Pi-built version of the popular open source network monitoring tool.

NagiosPi is available as a full image ready to be written to SD card, with the real configuration taking place once it's up and running. Let's get started.

Download NagiosPi

01 Windows users should write the extracted contents of the NagiosPi_v2.0.zip file to a formatted SD card using Win32 Disk Imager. Linux desktop users can use Disk Utility or the command line (**bit.ly/1z36sp8**). With the image written to SD, safely eject the card and insert it into your Pi before booting.

Log in to NagiosPi

02 As with most Pi projects, you'll probably want to operate via SSH, so check your router's list of connected devices to find the IP address and connect. You can also use a keyboard and monitor connected to your Raspberry Pi. The default username and password for NagiosPi is as follows: pi/raspberry.

Expand the filesystem

03 Before proceeding, run sudo raspi-config. You'll need to select the first option, Expand Filesystem, and wait a moment as the filesystem is expanded to the full size of the SD card.

Once done, select Change User Password to add some security to your NagiosPi, then select Finish and reboot.

Open in your browser

04 With the Pi rebooted, you'll be able to open the NagiosPi web console in your browser. Visit http://[your.IP.address. here] to see the available options.

Here you'll spot a menu of links in the top-left corner of the page, each accompanied with the username and password to sign in. Start with RaspControl.

Welcome to NagiosPi v1.0

NagiosPi Makes Monitoring Your Home or Small Business Easy! You can add hosts & services with Nconf. Get a visual display of your network health with Nagvis and easily make any database changes with PHPmyadmin.

Below you will find Some **Quick Links** to get you started.

- **Nagios** *(nagiosadmin/nagiosadmin)*
- **Nconf** *(nconf/nagiosadmin)*
- **NagVis** *(admin/admin)*
- **PHPmyadmin** *(root/nagiosadmin)*
- **RaspControl** *(admin/nagiosadmin)*

If you would like to remove the passwords from this page, Edit /var/www/index.html

Additional Resources:

- **Nagios:** Nagios.org
- **Nconf:** Nconf.org
- **Nagvis:** Nagvis.org
- **PHPmyadmin:** PHPmyadmin.net
- **RaspControl:** RaspControl GitHub Page

For Additional Details about the Image, Check Out The Authors Site.

Monitor your NagiosPi box

05 In the RaspControl section you'll get a flavour of just what Nagios can do. On the home screen you'll see general hardware information such as connectivity and system status, and as you flick through Details, Services and Disks you'll see what level of monitoring is possible.

View host status

06 Next, go to Nagios and pick Hosts. Here you will see the current status for the configured hosts, which is a combination of items detected on your local network and preset entities. Look for Current Network Status in the upper-left area of the console, just below this you will find alternate views.

Add a host to monitor

07 Open NConf to add the server you wish to monitor, using the 'Hosts – Add' button to input the device hostname, IP address and alias. Click Submit when done, then switch to 'Services – Add', where you can assign a name and check command (such as check_ping) to monitor.

Create configuration file

08 Each check must be set up individually. Some require the installation of NRPE (Nagios Remote Plugin Executor) on remote devices to interrogate and present full system details, but this isn't necessary for basic things like ping.

When you're done, click Submit, then Generate Nagios Config. Following this, select Deploy.

Monitor your server

09 In the NagiosPi window, select Services for a view of currently monitored servers and devices. For each listed device, there will be additional information that you drill down into by clicking Actions. We've only shown you the basics of NagiosPi – investigation will demonstrate just how powerful it really is!

What you'll need…

Android device
USB cable

Tether to an Android device

Need the internet on your Pi? Try out a physical tether to your Android device for online access

The portability of the Raspberry Pi is one of its most lauded features. Mini screens, mini wireless keyboard and mouse combos, portable batteries and more can get you out and about, but the internet is a stumbling block that you can't easily fix with an accessory. What you do also usually have with you is an Internet-connected magic pocket box called a smartphone that, with a bit of know-how, you can connect the Pi to and steal some internet from. Over the next two pages we will impart this know-how to get you using your Raspberry Pi on the Internet when you're on the go.

The easy way

01 Many smartphones have a Wi-Fi hotspot feature, which your Pi can easily attach to. First of all, turn the hotspot on and then boot into the Pi. Connect a wireless dongle and open up the wpa_gui in Preferences>Wi-Fi Configuration.

Scan for device

02 Click Scan to open up the scan window and then select Scan again from inside there. It should pick up your device – connect it as you would to any Wi-Fi network and the Pi will remember it for when it needs it next.

Set up tether

03 First connect your phone to your Raspberry Pi via a USB cable – depending on the amount of power your Pi has, it might have trouble charging your phone but it will still let you tether. In the tethering menu you can now activate USB tethering.

> "What you do also usually have with you is an internet-connected magic pocket box called a smartphone that you can connect the Pi"

Check connection

04 Your Android device will create an interface known as eth0 on the Raspberry Pi. You can check to make sure this is happening, and that it will let you tether, by opening up a terminal and typing the following:

```
$ ifconfig
```

Test connection

06 There's a few ways to test your connection. We'd usually stay in the terminal and ping **www.google.com**, which you can do, or you can click on the browser and see if it loads the page.

Interface settings

08 Here you'll find all the current network settings – yours might look different from ours depending on if you have added any fixed wireless settings or passthroughs. Using the same syntax as the eth0 line, add:

```
iface usb0 inet dhcp
```

Quick connect

05 You can connect from the terminal right now to access the Internet. You should be able to do this by typing the following into the terminal:

```
$ sudo dhclient usb0
```

This will automatically grab any available IP address that your phone will give to it.

Save the settings

07 Once you reboot your Raspberry Pi, it won't remember to automatically connect to the phone's tether. However, we can add an entry to its config so that it will try and do this in the future. From the terminal use:

```
$ sudo nano /etc/network/interfaces
```

Tether on the go

09 After a save and reboot, your Pi should now automatically connect to your phone, whether it's via Wi-Fi hotspot or a physical connection. It may draw a little more charge than usual while tethering, so be sure to keep an eye on your battery level.

What you'll need...

AA battery box
bit.ly/1FDiJGa

3-Amp UBEC
bit.ly/1HLKih7

3-Amp terminal strip

6x AA rechargeable batteries

Add a battery pack to your Raspberry Pi

Don't leave your Raspberry Pi behind – incorporate it into mobile projects by powering it up using humble AA batteries

Your Raspberry Pi's mobility is usually restricted by the length of the power lead. Rather than limiting it to your desk or living room, however, you can use it for mobile projects as diverse as launching it into near-Earth orbit or monitoring and automating your garden.

Of course, to do this you will need batteries, but adding battery power to your Raspberry Pi is simpler than you might have imagined. All that is required are six rechargeable AA batteries (or single-charge alkaline), a battery box with space for the batteries and a UBEC. The latter is a Universal Battery Elimination Circuit, a voltage regulator that will regulate the power supply and prevent damage to the Raspberry Pi, and can be bought for under £10.

> "You can use your device for mobile projects as diverse as launching it into near-Earth orbit"

Make your order

01 If you're buying your components online, you should be able to get them all within five days. However, if you're ordering offline (specifically the UBEC), you should avoid traditional electronics stores and instead visit a model enthusiast store, as these circuits are regularly used in RC devices.

Check your UBEC

02 Two types of UBEC are available to choose from. If you used the store that we suggest in the resources box to the left, you'll receive one with a micro USB power connector for easy connection to your Raspberry Pi. However, if you bought one from eBay then there is a strong chance that you will receive one with a 3-pin connector.

Move connector pins

03 In order to use the UBEC with a 3-pin connector, you'll need to alter the position of the pins so that they occupy the two outer slots. Just use a small jeweller's screwdriver to lever up the small plastic catch and remove the red wire from the central slot, before sliding into the unoccupied outer slot.

Connect to battery box

04 With five batteries in the battery box, connect it to the UBEC (red-to-red, black-to-black) by twisting the wires, soldering or employing a 3-amp terminal strip, cut down to two pairs. It can be cut to size using a modelling knife.

Add a battery to boot

05 With your Pi ready to use and your Wi-Fi dongle plugged in, connect the UBEC to the micro USB port and insert the sixth battery into the battery box. The Pi's power and status lights should indicate that the computer is booting up, which gives you a fully portable computer.

Connect the 3-pin UBEC

06 If you purchased the UBEC with the now-modified 3-pin connector, you'll need to connect this to the Raspberry Pi's GPIO header. Connect the positive +5V (red) connector to Pin 2 and the negative 0V connector to Pin 6.

Measure uptime

07 You should have already set up your Pi for SSH use, so connect to the device via Putty after giving it time to boot fully (at least 60 seconds). In the terminal, enter:

```
sudo dd bs=32m if=/Users/
rachelcrabb/Desktop/ArchLinux/
archlinux-hf-2013-02-11.img
of=/dev/disk1
```

This command will display the system uptime and also keep the Wi-Fi connection active.

Judge your uptime results

08 Uptime results depend upon the type of battery you use and the Raspberry Pi model. Single-charge batteries will last a little bit longer, but this is a more expensive option. Meanwhile, newer models have greater power requirements but run for less time. For more power, add more batteries!

Power extreme!

09 More batteries added in parallel should result in almost double the uptime (at least 16 hours on a 256MB Raspberry Pi Model A), but instead of alkaline or rechargeable batteries you might consider a modern lithium-based AA cell, which will last considerably longer than alkaline batteries.

Draw circuits with paint

What you'll need…

**Bare Conductive paint
(pen or tub)**

Male to female jumper wires

**An assortment of LEDs,
switches and resistors
(optional)**

Draw circuits with paint

Assembling circuits has never been so easy with the joys of conductive paint, enabling you to bring together art and electronics in a whole new way

Playing with electronics and physical computing is a very rewarding task. For a beginner though, the mess of wires and components can become very confusing quite quickly and things like soldering can be a safety concern when children are involved. Bare Conductive has taken the joy of electronics and made it far safer, easier and more versatile with their conductive paint. You can literally draw wires on paper with a paintbrush, use it for cold-soldering or a conductive adhesive and much, much more. There are not a great deal of boundaries to what you can do. Pair this paint with a microcontroller board and you could be creating interactive art, clothing and projects in no time.

Get your tools

01 Paint and a paintbrush aren't the first items that come to mind when you think about electronics, so you may be wondering where to get them from. Bare Conductive stock the paint and a selection of components in their shop (bareconductive.com/shop) but you will need to go somewhere else for art supplies. We would recommend trying a high street craft shop such as Hobbycraft (hobbycraft.co.uk) or a local independent.

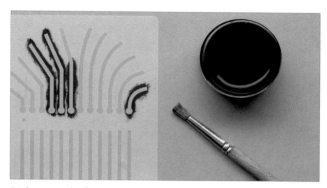

Pick your platform

02 The great thing about Bare Conductive paint is that, when dry, it works just like normal wiring! That means you can use it with any of your favourite microcontrollers like the Bare Conductive Touch Board, a Raspberry Pi or Adafruit's wearable FLORA platform. Or you can just use some small pin batteries and flashing LEDs for a standalone system.

Start to paint

03 You can paint Bare Conductive paint onto pretty much any surface – paper, fabric, walls, clothing, wood, plastic and much more. For really accurate shapes and results, the best idea is to create or purchase a stencil (paper stencils are easiest to make at home but use vinyl for the best edge finish).

Connect it up

04 There are plenty of ways to connect to the conductive paint (from battery packs for example) no matter what surface it's on, because once it is dry it acts just like an uninsulated wire. Therefore you can use wires glued on with the paint, paper clips, bulldog clips, alligator clips or even sewn-in conductive snaps for wearable projects.

Make repairs

05 The conductive paint is thick and when it's dry it becomes quite strong. These means you can use it to cold solder things together and repair any breakages. In other words, you could glue components into a circuit board or glue wires together and they would still function electrically.

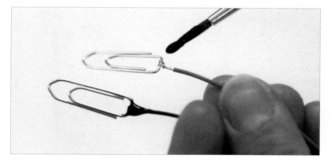

"The mess of wires and components can become very confusing"

Clean up

06 A lot of you are probably thinking that something as cool as conductive paint is going to be nasty stuff. Actually Bare Conductive paint is non-toxic, water-based and water-soluble, and can therefore be cleaned easily with soap and water.

Make it waterproof

07 This paint only comes in black and is not waterproof. However, the great thing is that you can use it underneath or alongside any regular paints, varnishes and waterproofing sprays in order to act as insulation – or just to add some colour into your designs.

Touch and sound

08 Bare Conductive paint can also be used as a capacitive surface, meaning you can use it for touch, gesture or proximity controls when it is paired with a suitable control board. Bare Conductive make their own called the Touch Board which has everything you need to start experimenting with touch and sound. It can even act as a MIDI controller, an interface or an instrument.

Send an SMS from your Raspberry Pi

What you'll need…

Raspberry Pi
Twilio account

Create a program that combines Twilio and simple Python code to enable you to send an SMS from your Pi to a mobile phone

Text messaging, or SMS (Short Message Service), has become a staple of everyday communication. What began life as a 40 pence message service is now offered by most tariff providers as an unlimited service used worldwide. Twilio, a cloud communications company, enables you to send SMS messages for free from your Raspberry Pi to a mobile phone using just six lines of code.

"Create other communication programs, such as making phone calls, recording a call, and retrieving data"

Set up your Twilio account

01 The first step of this project is to register for a Twilio account and Twilio number. This is free and will enable you to send an SMS to a registered, verified phone. Once signed up, you will receive a verification code via SMS to the registered phone. When prompted, enter this onto the Twilio site to authenticate your account and phone. Go to **twilio.com/try-twilio** and create your account now.

Register numbers

02 Your Twilio account is just a trial account unless you pay the upgrade fee, which means you can only send and receive communications from a validated phone number. Enter the phone number of the contact who you want to verify, ensuring that you select the correct country code. Twilio will text you a verification code and you will need to enter it into the website form and press submit.

The dashboard

03 Once registered and logged in on Twilio, visit the dashboard page, which will display your AccountSid and your Auth Token. These are both required to use the Twilio REST. Keep these secure and private, but be sure to make a note of them as you will need them for your Python program later.

Install the software

04 Now boot up your Raspberry Pi and connect it to the internet. Before you install the Twilio software, it is worth updating and upgrading your Pi. In the LX Terminal, type sudo apt-get update, then sudo apt-get upgrade. Once complete, type `sudo easy_install twilio` or `sudo pip install twilio` to install the software. (If you need to install pip, type `sudo apt-get install python-pip python-dev`, press Enter, then type `sudo pip install -U pip`.)

Twilio authentication

05 Now you are ready to create the SMS program that will send the text message to your mobile phone. Open your Python editor and import the Twilio REST libraries (line one, below). Next, add your AccountSid and Auth Token, replacing the X with yours, as you will find on your dashboard:

```
 from twilio.rest import
TwilioRestClient
    account_sid = "XXXXXXXXXXXXX
XXXXXXXXXXXXXXXXX"
                        # Enter
Yours
 auth_token =
"XXXXXXXXXXXXXXXXXXXXXXXXXXX"
                        # Enter
Yours
 client =
TwilioRestClient(account_sid,
auth_token)
```

Create your message

06 You will probably want to be able to change your text messages rather than send the same one. Create a new variable in your program called message. This will prompt you to enter the phrase that you want to send to the mobile phone. When the program runs, this is the message that will be sent:

```
 message = raw_input("Please
enter your message")
```

Add your numbers

07 To send the message, you need to add the code line below and your two phone numbers. The first number is your mobile phone number, which is registered and validated with Twilio (Step 2). The second number is your Twilio account number, which can be retrieved from your dashboard page under 'Call the Sandbox number'. Change the Sandbox number to your country location and remember to add the international country code.

```
     message =
client.messages.
create(to="+44YOURMOBNUMBER",
from_="+44YOURTWILIONUMBER",
body=message)
```

Send the message

08 Now send your message. The code below is not required, but is useful to indicate your message has been sent. Add the lines and save your program. Ensure your Raspberry Pi is connected to the internet and that your mobile is on, then run your program. You have just texted from your Raspberry Pi.

```
 print message.sid
 print "Your message is being
sent"
 print "Check your phone!"
```

Other API and codes

09 You can also create other communication programs, such as making phone calls, recording a call, and retrieving data including caller IDs and call duration. The API here also complements a wide range of programming languages, including Ruby, PHP, Java and Node.js (**twilio. com/api**) to name a few.

What you'll need…

OpenELEC openelec.tv
HDMI cable
USB IR receiver
IR remote
Case
Dedicated power supply
Optional USB storage

Make a Pi 2 HTPC

Finally create a more powerful and capable HTPC using the Raspberry Pi 2 and the excellent OpenELEC project

We know people who just have a Raspberry Pi for XBMC, now called Kodi. It's a great idea and a great use for the Pi – it works just well enough that you can easily play media locally or over the network. The biggest issue came with GUI response on the original Model Bs, and a lack of USB ports for connecting up everything that you want. While optimisation over the last few years has helped, the leap to Raspberry Pi 2 has basically solved all of these problems by giving you much more powerful hardware to play with. So if you're looking to upgrade or finally take the plunge, this handy guide will help you create the perfect Raspberry Pi 2 HTPC.

Choose the software

01 In the past, Pi HTPCs were just a choice between RaspBMC and OpenELEC. However, RaspBMC is on a bit of a hiatus and OpenELEC is your best bet for getting the most up-to-date software. There's not a massive difference between the two, as they both run XBMC.

Get the software

02 Head over to **openelec. tv** and look for the Download section. There's a specific Raspberry Pi section which is split up into original (ARMv6) Pi and the newer Raspberry Pi 2 (ARMv7). Grab the image file from this page for the Pi 2.

Install to card

03 Open up the terminal and use fdisk -l to determine where your SD card is located on your system. Something like /dev/sdb or /dev/mmcblk0 will be ideal. Navigate to the image using cd and install it with dd using:

```
$ dd bs=1M if=OpenELEC-RPi2.
arm-5.0.5.img of=/dev/
mmcblk0
```

First boot

04 Plug in your Raspberry Pi, either to your TV or to another screen just to begin with, and turn it on. OpenELEC will resize the SD card partitions and write a few extra programs before finally booting into Kodi.

Configure Kodi

05 Go through the basic wizard to get through the interface – if you are connecting via wireless you will need to go to OpenELEC in the System menu and activate the wireless receiver before selecting your network and then entering your password.

Add network shares

06 You can attach a portable hard drive or USB stick to the Pi for storage, but it is really to stream over the network. Go to File manager under System and Add source. Go to Browse and choose your network protocol to browse the network or alternatively, add it manually.

"It's a great use for the Pi – it works just well enough that you can easily play media locally or over the network"

Add network shares

07 Placement of your Raspberry Pi is important. As it's going to be out all the time, we highly recommend getting a case for it – the Pibow cases from Pimoroni are quite well suited for this type of use as they are sturdy and can be attached to the rear of some TVs.

IR sensors and controllers

08 Kodi can be controlled with a number of different things – including USB game controllers and compatible IR sensors. We've used FLIRC in the past, but if you have your Pi behind the TV, you'll need a sensor on a wire that can stretch to a useful position.

Future updates

09 OpenELEC has the excellent ability to update itself without needing you to reinstall it every few months, meaning you won't need to do much maintenance on it at all. Now you can sit back and enjoy your media much easier than before.

Print wirelessly with your Pi

Breathe new life into an old printer by using your Raspberry Pi as a wireless print server

Wireless printing has made it possible to print to devices stored in cupboards, sheds and remote rooms. You don't have to own a shiny new printer for this to work; old printers without native wireless support don't have to end up in the bin, thanks to the Raspberry Pi.

The setup is simple. With your Pi set up with a wireless USB dongle, you connect your printer to a spare USB port on the computer. With Samba and CUPS (Common Unix Printing System) installed on the Raspberry Pi, all that is left to do is connect to the wireless printer from your desktop computer, install the appropriate driver and start printing.

CUPS gives the Raspberry Pi a browser-based admin screen that can be viewed from any device on your network, enabling complete control over your wireless network printer.

Below Setting your Raspberry Pi to print wirelessly is a great way to get rid of annoying cables at your workstation

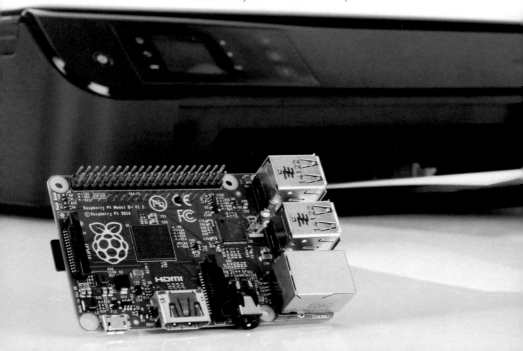

Check your printer works

01 Before starting, check that the printer you're planning to use for the project still works and has enough ink. The easiest way to do this is to check the documentation (online if you can't find the manual) and run a test print.

Detect your printer

02 With your Raspberry Pi set up as usual and the printer connected to a spare USB port, enter:

```
lsusb
```

This will confirm that the printer has been detected by your Raspberry Pi. In most cases you should see the manufacturer and model displayed.

Set up print admin

04 Set up the CUPS print admin tool. Boot into the GUI (startx) and launch the browser, entering 127.0.0.1:631. Switch to Administration, before ensuring that the 'Share printers' and 'Allow remote administration' boxes are selected. Select Add Printer and proceed to enter your Raspbian username and password.

Configure Samba for network printing

06 Using a Windows computer for printing? Samba will need some configuration. Open '/etc/samba/smb.conf' in nano, search (Ctrl+W) for '[printers]' and find 'guest ok' which you should change as follows:

```
guest ok = yes
```

Next, search for "[print$]." Then change the path as follows:

```
path = /usr/share/cups/drivers
```

Install Samba and CUPS

03 Install Samba on your Pi to enable file and print sharing across the entire network:

```
sudo apt-get install samba
```

Next, install CUPS:

```
sudo apt-get install cups
```

With a print server created, begin configuration by adding default user 'pi' to the printer admin group:

```
sudo usermod -a -G lpadmin pi
```

Add your printer

05 A list of printers will be displayed, so select yours to proceed to the next screen where you can confirm the details, add a name and check the Share This Printer box. Click Continue to load the list of printer drivers and select the appropriate one from the list.

Join a Windows workgroup

07 With these additions made, search for "workgroup" in the configuration file and then add your workgroup:

```
workgroup = your_
workgroup_name
```

```
wins support = yes
```

Make sure you uncomment the second setting so that the print server can be seen from Windows. Next, save your changes and then restart Samba:

```
sudo /etc/init.d/samba
restart
```

Accessing your printer

08 Meanwhile, it's a lot easier to access your wireless printer from a Linux, Mac OS X or other Unix-like system, thanks to CUPS. All you need to do is add a network printer in the usual way and the device will be displayed.

Add AirPrint compatibility

09 It's also possible to print wirelessly from your Apple iPad using Apple's AirPrint system. To do this, you need to add the Avahi Discover software:

```
sudo apt-get install avahi-
discover
```

Your wireless printer will now be discoverable from your iPad or iPhone and will be ready to print.

Control lights with your Pi

What you'll need…

Pi-Mote IR control board with RC sockets
bit.ly/1MdpFOU

Desk lamp

Accessories

Did you know…

Every device on the Internet is assigned an Internet Protocol address (IP address). This is a numerical label which is used to locate and identify each device within a network which may contain many thousands of devices. Most home network IP addresses start with the numbers 192.168, with your router being on 192.168.1.1.

Control lights with your Pi

The winter nights are getting longer; use a Pi and mobile device to remotely control your lights

The folks at Energenie have created some genius plug sockets that can be turned on and off via your Raspberry Pi. You can buy a starter kit which includes the RF transmitter add-on board and two sockets to get you started. The add-on board connects directly to the GPIO pins and is controlled with a Python library. Once everything is installed and set up, your Raspberry Pi can be used with the Pi-mote to control up to four Energenie sockets using a simple program. This tutorial covers how to set up the software, the sockets and how to adapt the program so that it can run on your mobile device.

Remote control
Take control of your home environment using your smartphone's browser

Light source
Any light source with a plug socket can controlled remotely

Above The Pi-Mote IR control board is hugely versatile and only costs £9.99

Set up

01 To get started, boot up your Raspberry Pi and load the LX Terminal, then update your software by typing:

```
sudo apt-get update
sudo apt-get upgrade
```

Depending on which version of the OS you're using, you may need to install the Python GPIO libraries. (Raspbian Jessie comes with this library pre-installed, so you can skip this step.) Type the following into the command line:

```
sudo apt-get install python-rpi.gpio
```

On completion, reboot your Pi. This will install the Python GPIO libraries, meaning you can access and control the pins with Python code.

"Your Pi can control up to four Energenie sockets using this simple program"

Install the Energenie library

02 Next, install the Energenie libraries. These enable the Pi-mote board and Raspberry Pi to interact with Python. In the LX Terminal, depending on which version of Python you are using, type either:

```
sudo apt-get install python3-pip
sudo pip-3.2 install energenie
```

...for Python 3, or:

```
sudo apt-get install python-pip
sudo pip install energenie
```

...for an older version. In the future, Energenie will update its software and you may need to run a check for updates to ensure that you have the most recent version. To update the software, type the code:

```
sudo pip install energenie -update
```

83

Fitting the Pi-mote

03 Before fitting the Pi-mote transmitter, shut down your Raspberry Pi with sudo poweroff. Next, unplug the power supply and fit the module onto your Raspberry Pi. The 'L' part of the board fits opposite the HDMI port. Power up the Pi and plug in one of your Energenie sockets in the same room or area that your Pi is in. The device's range is fairly good, but furniture, walls and other objects may sometimes block the transmission signal. You can test that the socket is working by plugging in something like a desk lamp and then pressing the green button that is located on the socket. This will trigger the socket on and off, turning the lamp on and off in turn.

Download the set-up code

04 Before the Raspberry Pi can interact with the socket and switch it on/off, it requires programming to learn a control code that is sent from the transmitter. Each socket has its own unique code so that you can control up to four individually. Energenie provides the set-up program which can be found inside your tutorial resources (available at **bit.ly/21ZRW4G**).

A quick test

06 Before you get to the task of creating your Python code to control your socket, it is always advisable to test that the socket is working correctly. Ensuring that the power is turned on at the wall plug and that the lamp is switched on, you can turn the lamp off by pressing the green button on the front of the Energenie socket. The lamp should turn back on again when the button is next pressed.

Set up your socket

05 Once you have downloaded the set-up program, run it. This should place the socket into 'learning mode', which will be indicated by the LED on the front of the socket housing slowly flashing. If it is not doing this, press and hold the green button for at least five seconds and release it when the LED starts to flash at one-second intervals. Run the program and it will send a signal out. Follow the on-screen prompts, pressing the return key when required.

When the code is accepted, success will be indicated with a brief flashing of the LED on the housing. If you have more than one socket to set up, simply use the same program and method to do so for as many times as required.

Code to turn the socket on

07 The Python Energenie library makes it incredibly easy to create a code to turn the socket on, which will then turn your lamp on. Before you know it, you will be using your Raspberry Pi to turn the kettle or the TV on or off!

Open your Python editor and start a new program. Next, import the Raspberry Pi GPIO library (line 1, below), then import the Energenie library (lines 2 and 3). Finally, add in the code to switch the socket on (line 4). Save and then run your program. The socket will turn on, you may hear a click, and then your lamp will come on.

```
import RPi.GPIO as GPIO
import energenie
from energenie import switch_on
energenie.switch_on(1)
```

Switching the socket on and off

08 Since you have not told the socket to turn off, it will stay on, which means the lamp will stay on forever (or until the bulb blows)! To turn the socket off after five seconds, import the time function at the start of your program (line 2, below), add the command to turn off the socket (line 5). Then add a pause with the sleep command (line 7) and finally turn off the lamp (line 8). Now save and run the program.

```
import RPi.GPIO as GPIO
import time
import energenie
from energenie import switch_on
from energenie import switch_off

energenie.switch_on(1)
time.sleep(5)
energenie.switch_off(1)
```

CSS and HTML

10 To make the web page presentable, you need to set up an HTML and a CSS file. HTML stands for HyperText Markup Language and is used to create web pages. Your browser reads HTML files and converts them into web pages, enabling images and objects to be embedded into the pages. Cascading Style Sheets, or CSS, is the code which describes how the web page will look; the presentation of the HTML content. It contains instructions on how the elements will be rendered. Here, it controls how the on and off options will be presented.

Create a new folder

11 With Flask installed, reboot your Raspberry Pi; type sudo reboot. Create a new folder called Mobile_Lights in the /home/pi folder. This is where you will save the Python program which controls the socket and lamp, the CSS and the HTML file. You can create the folder in the LX Terminal by typing mkdir Mobile_Lights or right-clicking in the window and selecting New Folder.

Web-based applications

09 It is possible to augment this hack so that you can turn the lamp on and off from a mobile device such as your phone, laptop or tablet. This makes the whole project more impressive, slick and fun. The first step is to set up your Raspberry Pi as a web server which will host and display a web page with the ON / OFF option. These buttons are interactive and control the socket. Open the LX Terminal and install pip and Flask:

```
sudo apt-get install pip
sudo pip install flask
```

"Using a mobile device such as your phone, laptop or tablet makes the whole project more impressive, slick and fun"

The HTML files

12 Open the Mobile_Lights folder and create a new folder called 'templates'. This folder is where the HTML file is saved that contains the structure for the website layout. The code names the web page tab and, most importantly, adds the links for the on and off option.

Open a text editor from your Start menu, or use nano and create a new file. Add the HTML below to the file and then save the file into the template folder, naming it 'index.HTML'. Remember, this is an HTML file and must end with the file extension .html:

```
<!doctype HTML>
<HTML>
<head>
<title>Light Controller</title>
<link rel="stylesheet" href="/static/style.css" />
<meta name="viewport" content="width=device-width, user-
  scalable=no" />
</head>
<body>
<div class="on"><a href="/on/">ON</a></div>
<div class="off"><a href="/off/">OFF</a></div>

</body>
</HTML>
```

Add some style

13 CSS is used to create and apply a 'button' style effect to the web page. Move back to the Mobile_Lights folder and create a new folder named 'static'. This is where the CSS file is saved. Create another new text file and add the code below, which sets out the 'style' for the web page. You can customise the colours of the buttons from line 20 onwards. Save the file as 'style.css' in the static folder.

```css
body {
    position: absolute;
    margin: 0;
    top: 0;
    right: 0;
    bottom: 0;
    left: 0;
    font-family: Arial, sans-serif;
    font-size: 150px;
    text-align: center;
}

div {
    display: block;
    width: 100%;
    height: 50%;
}

div a {
    width: 100%;
    height: 100%;
    display: block;
}

div.on {
    background: black;
}

div.on a {
    color: white;
}

div.off a {
    color: black;
}

a:link, a:visited {
    text-decoration: none;
}
```

Putting it all together

14 The final part of the setup is to write the Python script that combines the index.html and style.css files with the Energenie socket control code similar to the one used in Step 7.

Open IDLE and start a new window, add the following code and save into your Mobile_Lights folder, naming it 'mobile_lights.py'. Line 4 uses the route() decorator to tell Flask the HTML template to use to create the web page. Lines 7 and 11 uses app.route('/on/') and app.route('/off/') to tell Flask the function to trigger when the URL is clicked. In line 15 the run() function is used to run the local server with our application. The if __name__ == '__main__': makes sure the web server only runs if the script is executed directly from the Python interpreter and not used as an imported module.

```python
from flask import Flask, render_template
from energenie import switch_on, switch_off

app = Flask(__name__)

@app.route('/')
def index():
    return render_template('index.HTML')

@app.route('/on/')
def on():
    switch_on()
    return render_template('index.HTML')

@app.route('/off/')
def off():
    switch_off()
    return render_template('index.HTML')

if __name__ == '__main__':
    app.run(debug=True, host='0.0.0.0')
```

Find your IP address

15 Before you start the web server running, you will need to check the following:

- You have a folder set up called Mobile_Lights
- In the Mobile_Lights folder is a Python file named mobile_lights.py
- Also within the Mobile_Lights folder are two folders, one named templates which stores the index. HTML file and another folder named static which contains the file style.css

If everything checks out, then in the LX Terminal you can type sudo hostname –I. This will display the IP address of your Raspbery Pi – for example, 192.158.X.X. Make a note of it because this is the address you will enter into the web browser on your mobile device.

Start the web server

16 You have arrived at the point where you are ready to start the web server. Move to the Mobile_Lights folder by typing cd Mobile_Lights. Now run the Python mobile_lights.py program by typing sudo python mobile_lights.py. This starts up the web server, which is then ready to respond to the buttons that are pressed on the web page.

Turn your lights on and off

17 Grab your mobile device, smartphone or tablet and load the web browser. In the address bar enter the IP address that you noted down in Step 15. At the end of the address, add ':5000' – for example, 192.168.1.122:5000. The 5000 is the port number that is opened to enable the communication between your device and the Raspberry Pi. You will be presented with ON and OFF options, and you can now control the socket and whatever you have plugged in – kettle, radio, TV – all from your mobile device by simply pressing ON or OFF.

"You will be presented with ON and OFF options to control the socket"

Above You'll need to get the folder names correct so that files are saved properly

What you'll need…

Internet connectivity

Web browser

Google Coder
googlecreativelab.github.io/coder/
raspberrypi/sonicpi/teaching.html

Build your first web server

Use Google Coder to turn your Raspberry Pi into a tiny, low-powered web server and web host!

We're teaching you how to code in many different ways on the Raspberry Pi in this book, so it only seems fitting that we look at web development too.

There's a new way to use the web on the Raspberry Pi as well: internet giant Google has recently released Coder specifically for the tiny computer. It's a Raspbian-based image that turns your Pi into a web server and web development kit. Accessible easily over a local network and with support for jQuery out of the box, it's an easy and great way to further your web development skills.

Get Google Coder

01 Head to the Google Coder website, and download the compressed version of the image. Unpack it wherever you wish, and install it using dd, like any other Raspberry Pi image:

```
$ dd if=[path to]/raspi.img
of=/dev/[path to SD card] bs=1M
```

Plug in your Pi

02 For this tutorial, you'll only need to connect a network cable into the Pi. Pop in your newly written SD card, plug in the power and wait a few moments. If you've got a display plugged in anyway, you'll notice a Raspbian startup sequence leading to the command-line login screen.

Connect to Coder

03 Open up the browser on your main system, and go to **http://coder.local**. You may have to manually accept the licence. It will ask you to set up your password, and then you'll be in and ready to code.

Language of the web

04 Now it's time to create your own app or website. Click on the '+' box next to the examples, give your app a name and then click Create. You'll be taken to the HTML section of the app. Change the Hello World lines to:

▌ `<h1>This is a HTML header</h1>`

▌ `<p>This is a new block of default text</p>`

Styled to impress

05 Click on the CSS tab. This changes the look and style of the webpage without having to make the changes each time in the main code. You can change the background colour and font with:

▌ `body {`

▌ `        background-color: #000000;`

▌ `        color: #ffffff;`

▌ `}`

Querying your Java

06 The third tab allows you to edit the jQuery, making the site more interactive. We can make it create a message on click with:

▌ `$(document).click(function() {`

▌ `        alert('You clicked the website!');`

▌ `    }`

▌ `);`

Full code listing

HTML

Some simple HTML code that can point us to some important websites. The h2 tag is used to display the time thanks to Java

```
<h1>Welcome to the internet...</h1>
<h2></h2>
<p><a href="http://www.linuxuser.
co.uk">Linux User & Developer</a>
<p><a href="http://www.reddit.
com/">Reddit</a>
<p><a href="http://www.linuxfoundation.
org/">The Linux Foundation</a>
<p><a href="http://www.fsf.org/">Free
Software Foundation</a>
```

Java

We're calling the current time using jQuery in the JS tab so that we can ultimately display it on the webpage

We're going to display the time as a 12-hour clock in the first if statement, and use AM and PM to differentiate the time

We make the minutes readable by adding a 0 if it's below 10, then concatenate all the variables and assign to the tag h2

```
var d = new Date;
    var hours = d.getHours();
    var mins = d.getMinutes();
    if (hours > 12) {
        var hour = (hours - 12);
        var ampm = "PM";
    }
    else {
        var hour = hours;
        var ampm = "AM";
    }
    if (hours == 12) {
        var ampm = "PM";
    }
    if (mins > 9){
        var min = mins;
    }
    else {
        var min = "0" + mins;
    }
    var time = "The time is " + hour +
":" + min + " " + ampm;
    $("h2").html(time);
```

> "Coder is a Raspbian-based image that turns your Raspberry Pi into a web server and web development kit. It's an easy and great way to further your skills"

What you'll need…

Github repository
http://github.com/alexellis/pyPlaylist

pimoroni pHAT DAC

Soldering iron, flux & solder

Build your own networked Hi-Fi with a Pi Zero

Put the Pimoroni pHAT DAC together with a Pi Zero to create a networked Hi-Fi

Take advantage of the UK's online radio stations, Linux's popular Music Player Daemon, and utilise a responsive web-server to control it all. The full-sized Raspberry Pis have two built-in audio outputs: audio over HDMI cable and a 3.5mm headphone jack that can suffer interference and noise. The Pi Zero itself has no audio jacks but Pimoroni has come to the rescue and built a high-quality DAC (digital audio converter) using the same chip as the Hi-Fi berry (PCM5102A).

Did you know…

We wrote pyPlaylist with the Python flask framework, which is an ideal starting point for simple RESTful websites. The front-end code saves the screen from completely reloading by using jQuery to update the song or radio information. Bootstrap has been employed to make the pages responsive (compatible with your PC, phone and tablet). The code has been released under GPL, so why not fork the code and tweak it to your own needs?

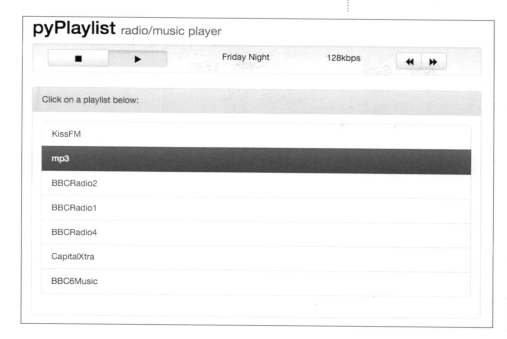

Solder the headers

01 The pHAT DAC comes with a 40-pin header, which you will need to solder. We consider a flux pen, work-lamp and thin gauge 60/40 solder essential for this. An optional RCA jack can also be bought to give a phono-lead output for older stereos.

Install drivers

02 The DAC relies on I2C, so we have to load some additional kernel modules. If you are running Raspbian then you can type in the following for a one-script installation over secure HTTP:

```
curl -sS https://get.pimoroni.
com/phatdac | bash
```
While HTTPS provides a secure download, curious types may want to review the script before running it.

Install Music Player Daemon (MPD)

03 Now go on to install the MPD package and enable it to start on boot. MPD will be the backbone of the project, providing playback of MP3s and internet radio stations. The MPC (client) software is also installed for debugging and setting up your initial playlists.

```
sudo apt-get install mpd mpc
sudo systemctl enable mpd
```

Clone and install pyPlaylist web-server

04 NpyPlaylist is a responsive (mobile-ready) web-server written with Python & Flask web framework. Once configured it will give us a way of controlling our Hi-Fi through a web-browser. The following will install pyPlaylist on Raspbian:

```
sudo pip install flask
python-mpd2
cd ~
git clone https://github.com/
alexellis/pyPlaylist
cd pyPlaylist
./raspbian_install.sh
```

"An optional RCA jack can also be bought to give a phono-lead output for older stereos"

Did you know…

In Raspbian/Jessie the controversial systemd software was added, giving a highly modular way of managing start-up scripts among other things. While systemd configuration files are now considered best practice, they can take time to fully understand. For that reason we would suggest using cron to start the script on reboot as a temporary measure.

```
crontab -e
@reboot /usr/bin/python
/home/pi/pyPlaylist/
app.py
```

Choose the radio stations

05 We have put together a list of some popular radio stations in the UK which can be run into MPD with the add_stations.sh file. You can edit this file or find your own from this site: **http://radiofeeds.co.uk**.

```
cd ~/pyPlaylist
./add_stations.sh
```

Review the stations

06 Each of the radio station are added into their own playlists – the **mpc ls** command shows which

of the playlists are available, as shown in the list below:

```
$ mpc ls
BBC6Music
BBCRadio1
BBCRadio2
BBCRadio4
CapitalXtra
KissFM
```

If you decide that you want to remove one of the stations then just type in the following:

```
mpc rm BBC6Music
```

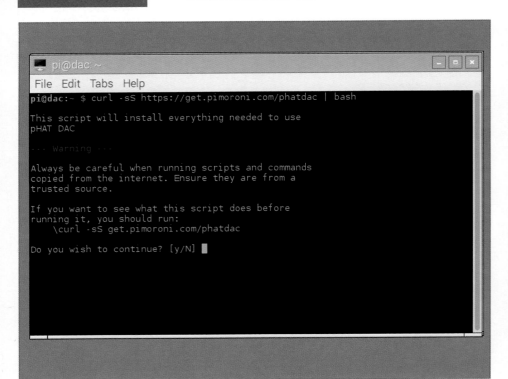

```
pi@dac:~ $ curl -sS https://get.pimoroni.com/phatdac | bash

This script will install everything needed to use
pHAT DAC

··· Warning ···

Always be careful when running scripts and commands
copied from the internet. Ensure they are from a
trusted source.

If you want to see what this script does before
running it, you should run:
    \curl -sS get.pimoroni.com/phatdac

Do you wish to continue? [y/N]
```

Start the web-server

07 Now that we have some stations, we can run the web-server from the pyPlaylist directory. Then open up a web browser to start playing a radio station. The following command reveals your IP address on Raspbian:

```
$ ./raspbian_get_ip.sh
192.168.0.20
```

Once you know the IP address, connect to the URL in a web-browser on port 5000, ie

```
http://192.168.0.20:5000/
```

Add a custom music playlist

08 Now put together a sub-directory with your music files under /var/lib/mpd/music/ and ensure that mpd:audio has access to read it. Then we update mpd's database, clear out the current playlist and add in all the tracks from the new directory (ambient), finally saving it as a new playlist.

```
mpc update
mpc clear
```

```
mpc ls ambient | mpc add
mpc save ambient
```

Finishing up

09 Now your music player is functioning, all that's left to do is to add some speakers, obviously! Almost anything with a RCA or 3.5mm input source will work for this purpose. That part we will leave up to you.
To take a look at the code here in full, go to **http://bit.ly/290maiH**. Go ahead and enjoy the tunes!

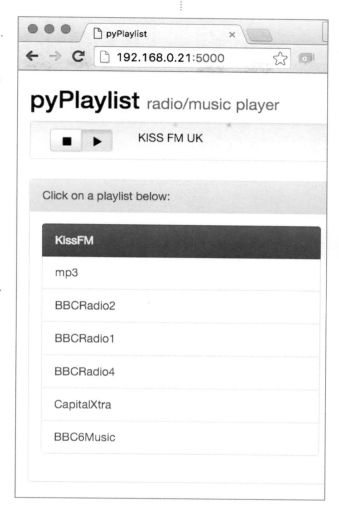

"Now that we have some stations, we can run the web-server from the pyPlaylist directory. Then open up a web browser to start playing a radio station"

What you'll need…

Latest Raspbian Image
www.raspberrypi.org/downloads

Breadboard

Connectors

Jumper wire

DSLR camera

Compatible shutter cable

Time-lapse camera trigger

Make shooting time-lapse video with your DSLR camera a cinch with our expert advice

You'd be forgiven for thinking that creating mesmerising time-lapse videos like those of Vincent Laforet (**www.laforetvisuals.com**) or John Eklund (**www.theartoftimelapse.com**) might be out of reach of the Average Joe. With the help of the Raspberry Pi and a sprinkling of Python code, though, that's no longer the case. In this guide we're going to trigger our DSLR camera to create pixel-perfect time-lapse imagery…

Set up the Raspberry Pi

01 For this tutorial we're assuming you're using a recent build of Raspbian. With the Raspberry Pi set up with a keyboard, mouse and monitor, open the terminal and type:

▌ sudo apt-get update

Install the RPi.GPIO library

02 Next we want to make sure your development environment is set up. Follow these steps to make sure you're all set. In the terminal, type:

▌ suda atp-get install python-dev
▌ sudo apt-get install python-rpi.gpio

Set up the Pi Cobbler

03 For this tutorial we've used a cheap prototyping breadboard and an Adafruit Pi Cobbler to give us easy access to the Raspberry Pi's GPIO pins. As you can see from the picture, the Cobbler straddles the centre-point of the breadboard and a ribbon cable connects the two.

Full code listing

```
import RPi.GPIO as GPIO
import time

print '\nWelcome to the Complete Manual Time-lapse Tool.'
print "Just tell us how many shots you'd like to take and ↵
the interval between them.\n"
print "Try googling 'time-lapse interval calc' if you need ↵
help deciding.\n"


def main():
    shots = raw_input('How many shots would you like to ↵
take?\n ->')
    interval = raw_input('How frequently do you want to ↵
take them (in seconds)?\n ->')

    if shots.isdigit() and interval.isdigit():
        shots = int(shots)
        interval = int(interval)

        print "You'll be shooting for %d minutes.\n" % ↵
(shots * interval / 60)
        answer = raw_input('Are you ready to proceed?(yes/ ↵
no):')

        confirm = answer.lower() in ['yes', 'y']

        if confirm:
            GPIO.setmode(GPIO.BOARD)
            GPIO.setup(16, GPIO.OUT)
            taken = 1
            print
            print 'Starting a run of %d shots' % (shots)
```

Manual focus
We won't be controlling the autofocus with our Python app, so set the focus to manual and select your camera settings in advance of the shoot

2.5mm to 3.5mm
We're using a cheap Canon EOS DSLR, so to trigger the shutter with the Raspberry Pi, all we need is a simple 2.5mm to 3.5mm cable

Pi Cobbler
We're using the Pi Cobbler as a breakout for the Pi's GPIO pins, making the build process easier (though it's not required)

```
        for i in range(0, shots):
            print
            print 'Shot %d of %d' % (taken, shots)
            taken +=1
            GPIO.output(16, GPIO.HIGH)
            time.sleep(0.5)
            GPIO.output(16, GPIO.LOW)
            time.sleep(interval)
        GPIO.cleanup()
    else:
        print "Let's try again (or press Ctrl + C to ↵
quit):\n"
        main()
    else:
        print "Oops - You can only enter numbers. Let's try ↵
again:\n"
        main()

    print
    print 'Thanks for using the Complete Manual Time- ↵
lapse Tool!\n'
    again = raw_input('Would you like to do another time- ↵
lapse? (yes/no):\n -> ')
    proceed = again.lower() in ['yes', 'y']

    if proceed:
        main()
    else:
        print '\nSee you next time!\n'
        quit()

if __name__ == '__main__':
    main()
```

Configure the breadboard

04 For the Raspberry Pi's GPIO to control the camera, we need to create a circuit between a pin on the GPIO (in this case pin 23 on the Cobbler – but it's actually physical pin 16) and the pin that connects to the 'head' or 'tip' of the camera cable that activates the shutter when connected. The base of the connector cable is always ground, so make sure you ground the 'GND' pin on the Cobbler and the middle pin on the audio jack. With the circuit complete, we can focus on the code.

The Time-lapse Photography Tool

05 We've created a small 55-line Python utility called The Linux User Time-lapse Photography Tool, which asks the user to input how many shots they'd like to take and the frequency they'd like them taken. It then takes that information and uses it in a For loop to activate the shutter using GPIO pin 16. If you'd like to use the project 'in the field' we'd recommend using the Android app ConnectBot to SSH into your RasPi for input and feedback. Don't forget to start your script with **sudo python¯ time_lapse_camera.py**

Creating a video

06 With your camera packed with images, we need to collect and output them as a video file. While it's possible on the Pi, copy them to an easily accessible folder on a separate Linux PC to make it much faster. We're going to use FFmpeg. With the terminal open in the folder where your images are stored, type: **ffmpeg -f image2 -i image%04d.jpg -vcodec libx264 -b 800k video.avi**. This assumes you have libx264 installed on your machine and the 'image%o4d. jpg' assumes the file format and the number of digits it's dealing with (in this case: 'picture0001.jpg').

What you'll need...

Wireshark
www.wireshark.or

**PiCam module or USB
webcam**

Get alerts with the Raspberry Pi baby monitor

Keep an eye on your little one while they sleep, thanks to your Raspberry Pi!

While you're settling down to enjoy a boxset, there's always that nagging feeling at the back of your mind – is the baby okay? We need to rely on baby monitors, specifically video monitors, in particular those that display footage on an app or by opening an IP address in a mobile browser. Add in some motion detection and alert software, and you've got an incredibly useful tool – which, the Raspberry Pi can do for a fraction of the cost. All you'll need is a Raspberry Pi (the newer the better), and a USB webcam or the PiCam (the NoIR infrared version is even more suited to nighttime use), and a device to view the streamed footage on.

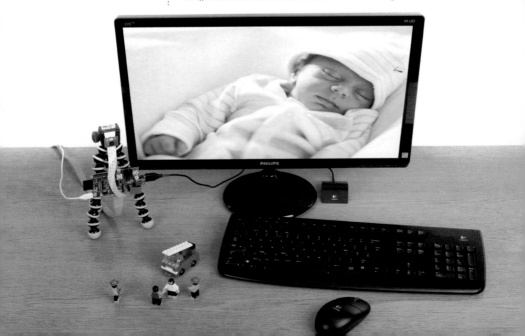

Survey the bedroom

01 Before you start installing and configuring your Pi, head to the baby's bedroom and take a look around. Where will you be placing the Raspberry Pi? Is it within reach of a power source? Do you need to connect an Ethernet cable, or is the wireless signal strong enough? It's vital at this stage to spend the necessary time planning the Pi's position in relation to power sources and network connectivity.

Enable the camera

02 If you're using the PiCam, this will be disabled by default. You can enable this in the raspi-config tool. This can be accessed in the GUI by opening Menu > Preferences > Raspberry Pi Configuration, where you should select the Interfaces tab and switch Camera to Enabled. Alternatively, run sudo raspi-config and choose option 6, Enable CameraFor USB webcams, use

```
sudo apt-get install
fswebcam
```

And test with

Test the camera

03 You don't want to set this project up to find that the camera doesn't actually work. Whether you're using a USB webcam or the PiCam, you'll need to run a command to test the camera. To confirm, use the GUI to browse to / home/pi and view the image.jpg file. This is preferable to checking in the command line, as you can ensure the image is not corrupt.

Install motion

04 The motion capture software, motion, can be installed after an update and upgrade of the Raspbian OS.

```
sudo apt-get update
sudo apt-get upgrade
sudo apt-get install motion
```

Older versions of motion will not start automatically, and display the "Not starting motion daemon" error message. To avoid this, you need to make sure you run the update and upgrade commands. If you're using the PiCam module, you'll also need a driver.

Activate PiCam driver

05 To activate the PiCam driver, you need to enter the following command:

```
sudo modprobe bcm2835-v4l2
```

This enables the PiCam to communicate with third party apps, such as motion. However, you'll need to invoke the driver every time you reboot, unless you add it to rc.local. Open the file in nano

```
sudo nano /etc/rc.local
```

Find an empty line before exit ="0"

and enter:

```
modprobe bcm2835-v4l2
```

Then CTRL+X to exit, and Y to save.

Auto-start motion

06 Begin by opening the motion configuration file.

```
sudo nano /etc/default/motion
```

Here, we need to instruct the software to start each time the Raspberry Pi boots. Find the value "daemon off" and change it to read:

```
daemon on
```

Hit CTRL+X to exit, tapping Y to confirm you wish to save the file, and Enter to continue.
Next, confirm the motion daemon works on a reboot by restarting your Pi

```
sudo reboot
```

Configure motion

07 The next step is to configure the motion software. This means setting the frame-rate (how often an image is captured), image dimensions (larger images will take up more resources, thereby slowing the monitor) and setting the video format. How you configure motion really depends on which model of Raspberry Pi you will be using for this project. First generation devices will still handle low-resolution images comfortably; for a hi-res feed, you should probably use the Raspberry Pi 3.

Edit the config file

08 Edit the config file
To begin configuration, just open motion.conf

```
sudo nano /etc/motion/motion.
conf
```

Use the CTRL+W shortcut to open search, find each of the following conditions, adding the values as specified:

```
daemon on
framerate 2
width 640
height 480
ffmpeg_video_codec mpeg4
stream_localhost off
control_localhost off
```

If you're recording in a dark room, you can adjust the brightness and contrast. With the changes made, hit CTRL+X to exit, confirming with Y and Enter.

Assign ownership to target directory

09 You may find that the camera stops streaming images after a short time. This is a permissions issue, one that causes a few images to appear on your screen before the whole thing times out. Overcome this with

```
sudo chown motion: /var/
lib/motion
```

You can also set a custom file path in motion.conf. Look for target_dir and change as appropriate. Remember to save the file and restart motion when you're done.

Start and test your baby monitor

10 We now almost have a fully working baby monitor. At this stage, all that is left to get the baby monitor up and running is to launch the motion:

```
sudo service motion start
```
You should be able to browse to the feed by entering the IP address of your Raspberry Pi in a mobile browser. This would typically be something like

```
192.168.0.10:8081
```

Check this on multiple devices on your home network to confirm that it works.

Adjust motion detection

11 It's unlikely that you will find that motion detection works right away. In order to adjust this for the environment you have the Pi baby

monitor set up in, open

```
sudo nano /etc/motion/motion.
conf
```

and use CTRL+W to search for "Motion Detection Settings".
Here you'll find various conditions with values that you can adjust, such as threshold and area_detect_value. These will require some patient tweaking for the best results.

Make motion beep

12 To aid in tweaking the detection, you can enable a beep to sound when movement is captured. As a project like this needs some calibration to get the best results, this is a useful feature.
Again, this setting is found in motion.conf. Search for "quiet on" and change the setting to read

```
quiet off
```

Remember to undo this when you're happy with the movement capture, as it may disturb the little one!

Adjust image quality

13 While you can alter dimensions of the images captured by the PiCam board, it's important to be careful with the figures you enter in motion.conf. For instance, a dimension of 133x255 pixels probably won't work. Dimensions need to be multiples of 4. For larger options, look at 1280x800 or 1920x1080.
Not only will larger images impact bandwidth, they'll make the resulting AVI file larger.

Check saved images

14 To confirm the quality of the images captured by the Raspberry Pi baby monitor, boot into the GUI (or install tightvncserver and remote connect) and browse to /var/lib/motion to see how they are turning out. This should give you the info you need to adjust the dimensions of the captured images.

Troubleshoot camera connectivity

15 There's no guarantee that motion will work straight away. If no images are found, or you can't connect to the stream, run:

```
tail -f /var/log/syslog
```

and

```
dmesg | tail
```

This will display any issues that the process is currently having, which is intended to (and hopefully will!) help you diagnose and resolve any problems.

Most issues will be driver-related, so keep this in mind with USB webcams. Press CTRL+Z to end.

Name your images

16 Images collected by the motion software can be configured with a specific naming convention, based on date and time.

You can find these listed under "target base directory" in motion.conf. For instance, you can specify a folder for new images, based on date:

```
%Y_%m_%d/%v-%Y%m%d%H%M%S-%q1
```

Note the "/" – both directory and

images will be named according to date, with images also labelled with the timestamp.

Go beyond your home network

17 Wouldn't it be great to monitor your child's sleep from your favourite restaurant? You can do this by installing the No-IP software on your Raspberry Pi.

This software enables you to get around the fact that your ISP won't give you a dedicated IP address without paying a hefty premium, by installing a client app that enables you to view the baby monitor outside your home network.

Head to **www.noip.com** and check their knowledge base for details.

What you'll need…

A portable hard drive

Raspbian
www.raspberrypi.org/downloads

PC with a desktop environment with Deluge
www.deluge-torrent.org

Build an always-on torrent box

Get the latest distros, packages and test builds faster with a low-power, mini torrent box

Torrenting your open source software has a number of advantages – it can be faster, alleviates bandwidth and allows you to share back with the community. Distros, packages and more are available via torrents, and the Raspberry Pi makes for a great tiny, low-wattage, always-on torrent box to better manage your files.

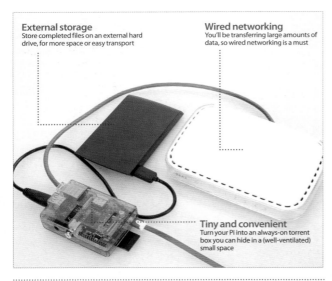

External storage
Store completed files on an external hard drive, for more space or easy transport

Wired networking
You'll be transferring large amounts of data, so wired networking is a must

Tiny and convenient
Turn your Pi into an always-on torrent box you can hide in a (well-ventilated) small space

"The Raspberry Pi makes for a great tiny, low-wattage, always-on torrent box to better manage your files"

Install Raspbian

01 Raspbian works just fine for our torrent box. Install the image on an SD card and go through the basic setup process, making sure to enable SSH in the advanced options and to disable the desktop.

Remote access

02 Type ifconfig into your Pi's command line to find the IP address. At this point you can unplug the monitor and set it up remotely, but either way you can now access the Pi by typing:

```
$ ssh [user]@[IP address]
```
…and entering your password to log in.

Mount hard drive

03 Unless you plan to reformat your portable drive, you'll need to install NTFS support onto your Pi. Type in:

▌ $ sudo apt-get install ntfs-3g

Add the hard drive to **/etc/fstab** (open it with sudo nano /etc/fstab) by adding the line:

▌ /dev/[hard drive address] [mount point] auto noatime 0 0

Use fdisk to find the name of the storage, and create a mount point such as /home/pi/torrents with mkdir. Reboot for it to mount.

Install Deluge

04 We'll use Deluge for our torrents. Install it with:

▌ $ sudo apt-get install deluged deluge-console

Now start and then stop Deluge so it creates a config file we can edit with:

▌ $ deluged
▌ $ sudo pkill deluged

And finally, run the following to copy the config file in case we mess up:
$ cp ~/.config/deluge/auth ~/.config/deluge/auth.old

Basic configuration

05 Edit the file with:
▌ $ nano ~/.config/deluge/auth

And add to the bottom:

▌ [user]:[password]:10
…to restrict access.
Now start it up with:

▌ $ deluged
▌ $ deluge-console

Remote connection

06 Now you're in the client, type the following three commands:

▌ config -s allow_remote True
▌ config allow_remote
exit

Restart the Deluge daemon with:

▌ $ sudo pkill deluged && deluged

Now open the graphical client on your Linux PC.

Remote interface

07 Go to Edit>Preferences> Interface, then disable Classic Mode and restart Deluge. Click Add on the Connection Manager, and enter the IP in Hostname and the user we set up earlier. Click Connect to see any torrents you have downloading or uploading.

Download location

08 Go to Edit again and then Preferences, and change to the Downloads tab if it's not on there already. Set the download location to the directory we mounted the hard drive to, and enable 'Auto add .torrents', setting it to any destination if you plan to dump torrents to the Pi.

Start on boot

09 An init script from Ubuntu can be used to have Deluge start on boot. Download it with:

▌ $ sudo wget -O /etc/default/deluge-daemon http://bit.ly/13nKOSj

Open **/etc/default/deluge-daemon** with nano and change the username to the one we set up earlier. Save it, then download the full init script and update with:

▌ $ sudo wget -O /etc/init.d/deluge-daemon http://bit.ly/13nKKlz

▌ $ sudo chmod 755 /etc/init.d/deluge-daemon

▌ $ sudo update-rc.d deluge-daemon defaults

What you'll need…

Raspbian Wheezy
HDMI cable
Monitor

Stream Internet TV to your Pi

Get your favourite shows and video podcasts streamed automatically to your TV with Miro

Finding the content you're interested in viewing can take a while. Whether you're looking for Internet TV stations, video podcasts, audio podcasts or shows syndicated online, taking the time to find and download them can be slow going, particularly if you have a busy lifestyle. You might even have no time to watch after you've waited for the download.

Thanks to the Miro media management software, we can automate all of this, and with the software running on a Raspberry Pi, you can easily build a compact system for downloading and playing back shows that you have an interest in. We're talking targeted TV on demand, which makes this project ideal for staying up to date with particular news and trends on a certain topic.

Set up your Pi with Raspbian

01 Sadly, Miro cannot run on Raspbian Jessie, so make sure you're using Wheezy, available via **raspberrypi.org/downloads/raspbian**. Ensure your Pi is connected to a TV or display via HDMI. As Miro is a desktop application, you'll need your mouse and keyboard connected to configure it.

Install Miro

02 With Wheezy flashed to your SD card and your Pi booted up, open Terminal and enter:

```
sudo apt-get install miro
```

Installation will take a few moments. Once complete, you'll find Miro in Menu>Sound and Video. Click it to get started.

Set Miro to launch at startup

03 Make sure Miro app is configured to launch at startup. Open File>Preferences>General and check 'Automatically run Miro when I log in' and 'When starting up Miro remember what screen I was on when I last quit'. Also set your Pi to boot into X using the raspi-config utility.

Check for content

04 Switch to the Podcasts tab and place a check in the box labelled 'Show videos from podcasts in the Videos section'. On the right-hand side of the window, set your preferred frequency for checking for new content. Miro will poll your favourite websites and feeds based on this setting.

Above Miro gives you a decent playback interface and excellent export options for converting videos for other formats

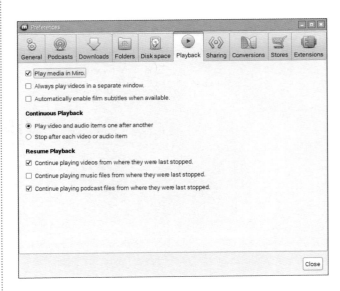

Configure playback settings

05 Move now to the Playback tab, and check Play media in Miro. This limits reliance on other apps, which may drain resources. You should also click the Play video and audio items one after another radio button, and under Resume Playback, check the first and third items.

"The more links you add, the more regularly updated content will be downloaded to your media manager"

Source videos and podcasts

06 With Miro now set up and ready to play back the video and audio content that you want to enjoy, it's time to find some! The best way to do this is to just check the websites that you regularly use for video and audio podcasts (preferably the former) and then copy the XML link.

Add podcast feeds

07 In Miro, open up File>Add Podcast and then paste the podcast feed URL into the dialog that appears, clicking Create Podcast when you're done.

The more links you add, the more regularly updated content will be downloaded to your Pi-powered Miro media manager, ready to watch or listen to on demand.

First time use

08 Remember earlier in the tutorial when we instructed Miro to behave in a particular way when it launched? It's time to set that behaviour now.

The process is started by opening the Videos view in the left-hand pane of the Miro window, and then playing the first video. Each time you boot your system, Miro will jump to this view and immediately begin playing your content, making sure you get up and running quickly and smoothly.

Avoid YouTube

09 As good a solution as Miro is to building a video podcast streaming center, displaying material that you're interested in on demand, it's sadly just no good for videos on YouTube. This doesn't really restrict you too much as there are plenty of other media outlets to cover, but it's worth mentioning if you're a frequent YouTube watcher. This is a shame, but shouldn't impact the way you use it – your Raspberry Pi now downloads focused content on demand.

Above You can subscribe to all sorts of content, from Internet TV channels to comedy and news podcasts

Checking for new content

10 It is tempting to set a regular frequency for your content checking in File>Preferences>Podcasts, but note that checking too regularly is going to result in resources being hogged temporarily, which may result in an interruption if you happen to be actually watching something when Miro checks for new content. Limit polling to hourly or daily checks.

What you'll need...

Raspberry Pi 2 or 3 with Raspbian Jessie

Wi-Fi dongle (if using Raspberry Pi 2)

Display (official 7-inch Touchscreen Display recommended)

Phillips screwdriver

Frame and/or stand (suitable options for the official touchscreen display are available at Pimoroni and other dedicated Pi hardware and accessory suppliers)

Scripts
https://github.com/samuelclay/Raspberry-Pi-Photo-Frame

Make a Pi-powered digital picture frame

Use a Raspberry Pi to create your own fully configurable digital picture frame, complete with touchscreen display

Digital picture frames that display a selection of your favourite photos were quite popular for a time, but are now seemingly available only as free gifts when signing up to magazine subscriptions. These tablet-like devices often made for interesting talking points, but were often let down by low memory, a poor user interface, or both.

We don't have to worry about either of those problems with this project. Here we are going to set up a Raspberry Pi with some photo-displaying software, connect a touchscreen display, place it in a suitable stand, and sit back to enjoy the results. Better still, with this set-up, we'll be able to pull images from a range of online and offline sources, giving us some great variety.

Prepare your Pi

01 You'll save a lot of time with this project if you ensure that wireless networking is set up, and SSH is enabled. Do both via the Raspbian Jessie desktop – you'll find the new Raspberry Pi Configuration utility in Menu>Preferences, where you can enable SSH in the Interfaces tab.

Connect the display

02 With a towel on your desk to avoid scratches, connect the Raspberry Pi to the back of the 7" Touchscreen Display, making sure that the cables are connected correctly. (Older releases require you to also connect and mount the display board). Secure with screws, and then mount in stand.

Did you know…

You shouldn't feel restricted by the photos you can display on your Raspberry Pi picture frame. Various options exist for you to pull images down from popular web services, such as Flickr or Facebook. To do this, you'll need a dedicated Python script, which has happily already been written for you. Head to Samuel Clay's Github to download them, but don't add the scripts to rc.local until you've confirmed they work.

"Set up a Raspberry Pi with some photo-displaying software"

Prepare your photos

03 Naturally, you'll need a collection of photos to display on the Pi-powered digital picture frame. We have different options here (see boxout, page 107) but recommend you start with photos stored on your Pi, ones that have been copied via USB, via a network drive, or downloaded through your browser.

Set up your Pi picture frame

04 To configure the Raspberry Pi as a picture frame, we first need to prevent the screen from switching off. This means editing the lightdm.conf file.

```
sudo nano /etc/lightdm/
```

lightdm.conf

Add this line under [SeatDefaults]:

```
xserver-command=X -s 0 -dpms
```

When done, save and exit with Ctrl+X, then reboot:

```
sudo reboot
```

Install feh

05 NImage viewing software feh is the best option for building a simple Pi picture frame, so install this.

```
sudo apt-get install feh
```

Once installed, instruct feh where to find the images, changing /media/

STORAGE/test with your directory path, eg.

```
DISPLAY=:0.0 XAUTHORITY=/home/
pi/.Xauthority /usr/bin/feh -q
-p -Z -F -R  60 -Y -D 15.0 /
media/STORAGE/test
```

"Naturally, you'll need a collection of photos to display on the Pi-powered digital picture frame"

Save the script

06 The previous script should have prompted the Raspberry Pi picture frame to begin displaying images from the specified folder, for 15 seconds each. To force this to start at boot, we need to add it into a script. Create this with:

```
sudo nano /home/pi/start-
picture-frame.sh
```

Add the following:

```
#!/bin/bash
DISPLAY=:0.0 XAUTHORITY=/home/
pi/.Xauthority /usr/bin/feh -q
-p -Z -F -R  60 -Y -D 15.0 /
media/STORAGE/test
```

Exit and save, then test with:

```
bash /home/pi/start-picture-
frame.sh
```

Make picture frame run at boot

07 The script can now be set to run at boot. Open

```
sudo nano /etc/rc.local
```

…and before exit 0, add:

```
sleep 10
su - pi -c '/bin/bash /home/
pi/start-picture-frame.sh &'
```

Save and exit.

Reboot your Pi and test

08 Now you're pretty much done! To test it out, use the usual sudo reboot command to restart the Raspberry Pi and check that the device boots straight into picture frame mode. If you experience any problems, check that your commands have been entered correctly, and in the right places using lightdm.conf and rc.local.

Stop the picture frame

09 Should you need to stop the picture frame software at any time, this can be done with the following simple command:

```
sudo pkill feh
```

As long as the images you prepared for your picture frame don't take up too much space on the disk, they should load up without any problems.

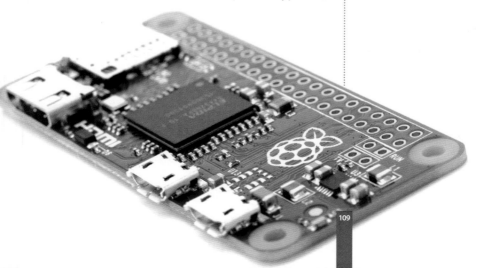

What you'll need…

A toy RC car with two channels (steering and drive)

Adafruit PWM I2C servo driver

Female-to-female jumper cables

5V battery power bank

Estimated cost: £60 / $100

Components from
www.modmypi.com

Build a Raspberry Pi-powered car

Make use of cutting-edge web technologies to take control of a remote controlled car with a smartphone or tablet…

Did you know...

You can make this project work with just about any remote controlled car. Follow the guide for more details.

Web technologies are moving forward at a huge pace, cloud technologies are bringing mass computing to individuals, and hardware has reached a perfect moment in time where sensors, displays and wireless technology have all evolved into efficient and affordable devices. We truly are at a point where nearly anyone can take an idea from nothing to a working product in a week and at very little cost. Just like this project, which is fun, quick and easy to build on and a fantastic way to learn. We're going to grab an old remote-control car, rip off its radio receiver and replace it with the Raspberry Pi, hook it up on the network, fire up a bleeding-edge web server and then get your smartphone or tablet to control it by tilting the device. By the end of this, not only will you have a fun toy, you will have learnt about the basic technologies that are starting to power the world's newest and biggest economy for the foreseeable future.

Raspberry Pi-controlled car build process

To help our toy car come to life using the latest web technologies and our credit card-sized computer, we're going to need to make some pretty significant changes to its workings. Fortunately, the most complex aspects of the build can be accomplished with a couple of affordable purchases, namely a servo controller board to take care of the steering and throttle, and a 5V battery pack to keep the Raspberry Pi running smoothly.

Identify and remove old radio

01 This project is effectively replacing the car's normal transmitter and receiver. Notice the three sockets on the original receiver: one goes to the motor controller and one to the steering servo. Some remote-control cars also have separate battery for the electronics, but those (especially with an electronic speed controller with BEC) get their 5V power supply directly from the speed controller, saving on components. If you don't have a speed controller with 5V BEC, you'll need to get a 5V supply elsewhere. Many shops sell 5V battery power supplies – often as mobile phone emergency top-ups. www.modmypi.com sells a suitable 5V battery power bank for under £20 and you should get a couple of hours of use from your Raspberry Pi.

Power up
This 5V battery pack keeps our Raspberry Pi running for a good few hours

Servo control
Adafruit PWM I2C servo driver board from www.modmypi.com

Pi-powered
The Raspberry Pi sits front and centre to keep it as safe as possible

Pick a car
You can use pretty much any affordable car for this project

Attach the servo cables to the new controller

02 We soldered our 16-channel I2C servo controller board from **www.modmypi.com** as per its instructions and simply plugged channel 0 (steering) and channel 1 (motor) headers onto it. There are six cables in total: the bottom two are ground, the middle two are the power and the top two are the PWM (pulse-width modulation) signals. This is a good time to think of places to mount the extra components and the best fixing method seems to be sticky-back Velcro.

Connect the I2C bus to the Raspberry Pi

03 We're using the Raspberry Pi's I2C bus to control the servo interface board, which only needs four cables – they all go between the Raspberry Pi and the servo controller board as pictured. Visit **http://bit.ly/N3nq4J** for a tutorial on how to set up I2C on the Raspberry Pi.

From top to bottom we need to use the 1. GND, 2. SCL, 3. SDA and 4. VCC, which map directly to the same ports on the Raspberry Pi. Essentially this is power, ground and two communication channels.

Hook it up to the Raspberry Pi

04 On a Rev 1 Raspberry Pi, the cables look the same. Though the Rev boards have different labelling, the physical pins are in the same place. Bottom left (closest to the RasPi power connector) is the 3.3V power; next to that is the SDA header, which is the data channel. Next to that in the bottom right is the SCL channel, which controls the clock of the I2C devices. And finally – on the top-right port – is the Ground. We recommend printing a labelled image of the GPIO pins.

Overview of the main components

05 You should now have the servo board in the middle with the steering servo and speed controller on one side and the Raspberry Pi on the other. The motor is connected to the other end of the speed controller (that end should have much thicker wires); the speed controller also has two thick wires going to the main car's battery – in this case a 7.2V NiCad. We now have two very separate power systems with the high current motors on one side and the low current electronics on the other. Let's make sure it stays that way.

Find everything a home

06 We can now put it together. Use plenty of sticky-back Velcro, tie wraps or elastic bands to keep everything secure and find spaces in the car's body to hide the wires where possible. While it is possible to stick or screw the Raspberry Pi directly to the car, we recommend to use at least the bottom half of a case for added protection and ease of access. Insert your SD card, network cable or Wi-Fi dongle and power supply. Sit back and admire your hacking skills.

What you'll need...

A RasPi car, ready to go

An internet connection

A reasonably modern smartphone/tablet

Pi car source code
github.com/shaunuk/picar

Control your Raspberry Pi-powered car

Control a toy car with a smartphone and the latest web technologies

Now that we have our fantastic Raspberry Pi-powered car all wired, charged and ready to go, it's time to make it come alive. We're using the best web technologies that the JavaScript programming language offers, to harness the natural movement of your hand and wirelessly drive the vehicle.

Each little movement of your hand will trigger an event that calculates what the car should do and then sends it over a socket connection. If all goes to plan you should have complete control over your vehicle.

Did you know...

Our code will send instructions to our car over twenty times per second. It will be very responsive to drive!

Download and install the software

01 First of all, you will need to the I2C connectivity working. Next we'll need to find a home for our new project code – how about /var/www/picar? Type `sudo mkdir /var/www/picar` in the terminal to make the directory and then change into that directory: `cd /var/www/picar`

Now, to download the project using Git, type `sudo git clone http://github.com/shaunuk/picar`. If you haven't got Git, install it with `sudo apt-get install git`.

This will download the custom software for driving the car, but we still need the web server and some other bits before we can start burning rubber...

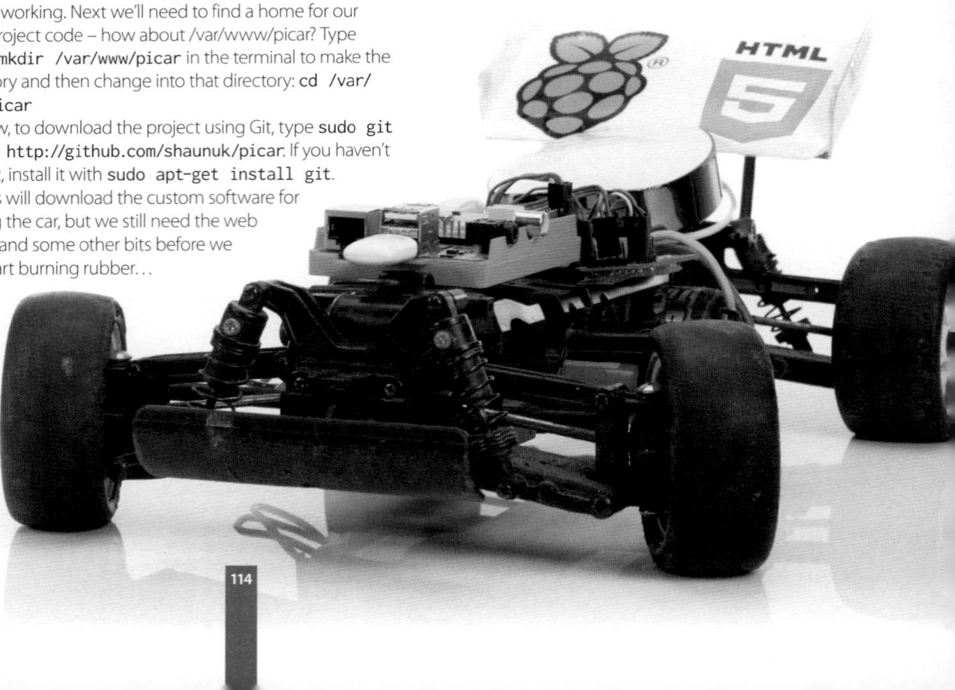

Below All you need to finish off your project is access to a smartphone or tablet

Download and install Node.js

02 Next we're using Node.js and its package tool, the Node package manager (npm). Type `sudo wget http://nodejs.org/dist/v0.10.21/node-v0.10.21-linux-arm-pi.tar.gz`. This will download a fairly recent version of Node.js – the version Raspbian has in its repositories is way too old and just doesn't work with the new technologies we're about to use. Extract the node package by typing:

▌ `sudo tar -xvzf node-v0.10.21-linux-arm-pi.tar.gz`

Configure Node.js

03 To make it easy to run from everywhere, we will create symbolic links for Node and npm binaries. Type `sudo ln -s /var/www/node-v0.10.21-linux-arm-pi/bin/node /bin/node` and then `sudo ln -s /var/www/node-v0.10.21-linux-arm-pi/bin/npm /bin/npm`. Then, to get the extra modules, type `npm install socket.io node-static socket.io adafruit-i2c-pwm-driver sleep optimist`

Below You need to adjust some of the variables to control your particular remote controlled car setup

Get to know the project

04 Now we have everything, you should see three files: the server (app.js), the client (socket.html) and the jQuery JavaScript library for the client. The server not only drives the servos, but it is a web server and sends the socket.html file and jQuery to the browser when requested – it's a really neat and simple setup and just right for what we're trying to achieve.

Test the servos

05 Our handy little program (app.js) has a special mode just for testing. We use two keywords here: beta for servo 0 (steering) and gamma for servo 1 (motor control). Type node app.js beta=300. You should see the front wheels turn. Now the numbers need experimenting with. On our example, 340 was left, 400 was centre and 470 was right. Do the same for the motor by typing node app.js gamma=400 and take note of the various limits of your car.

"We're using the best web technologies that the JavaScript programming language has to offer"

Configure sensible defaults

06 Now you know what your car is capable of, we can set the defaults in app.js and socket.html. Edit app.js and find the section that says 'function emergencyStop'. Adjust the two numbers to your car's rest values. Then open socket.html and adjust the predefined values under 'Define your variables here'.

Going for a spin

07 We're almost ready to try it out, but you need to know the IP address of your Pi car, so type ifconfig at the terminal. Then fire up the app by typing node app.js. Now grab the nearest smartphone or tablet, making sure it's on the same network as your Pi. Open the web browser and go to **http://[your IP address]:8080/socket.html**. You should get an alert message saying 'ready' and as soon as you hit OK, the gyro data from your phone will be sent to the car and you're off.

Full code listing

socket.html

```
<html>
<head>
<script src="jquery-2.0.3.min.js"
language="javascript"></script>
<script src="/socket.io/socket.io.js"></
script>
<meta name="viewport" content="user-
scalable=no, initial-scale=1.0, maximum-
scale=1.0;" />
<script>
//------ Define your variables here
var socket = io.connect(window.location.
hostname+':8080');
var centerbeta = 400; //where's the middle?
var minbeta = '340'; //right limit
var maxbeta = '470'; //left limit
var multbeta = 3; //factor to multiply the
// raw gyro figure
var centergamma = 330;
```

```
var ajustmentgamma = 70; //what do we do to
the angle to get to 0?
var mingamma = 250; //backwards limit
var maxgamma = 400; //forward limit
var multgamma = 1; //factor to multiply the
//raw gyro figure by to get the desired
//rate of acceleration
window.lastbeta='0';
window.lastgamma='0';
$(function(){
  window.gyro = 'ready';
  alert('Ready -- Lets race !');
});
window.ondeviceorientation = function(event)
{
  beta = centerbeta+(Math.round(↵
event.beta*-1)*multbeta);
  if (beta >= maxbeta) {
    beta=maxbeta;
  }
  if (beta <= minbeta) {
    beta=minbeta;
```

```
   }
gamma = event.gamma;
   gamma = ((Math.round(event. ↵
gamma)+ajustmentgamma)* multgamma)+ ↵
centergamma;
//stop sending the same command more than
once
send = 'N';
if (window.lastbeta != beta) { send = 'Y' }
if (window.lastgamma != gamma) { send = 'Y'
}
window.lastbeta=beta;
window.lastgamma=gamma;
if (window.gyro == 'ready' && send=='Y')  {
//don't send another command until ready...
   window.gyro = 'notready';
     socket.emit('fromclient', { beta: beta
↵ gamma: gamma } );
     window.gyro = 'ready'; }}
```

app.js

```
//declare required modules
var app = require('http').
createServer(handler)
   , io = require('socket.io').listen(app)
   , fs = require('fs')
   , static = require('node-static')
   , sys = require('sys')
   , PwmDriver = require('adafruit-i2c-pwm-
driver')
   , sleep = require('sleep')
   , argv = require('optimist').argv;
app.listen(8080);
//set the address and device name of the ↵
breakout board
pwm = new PwmDriver(0x40,'/dev/i2c-0');
//set pulse widths
setServoPulse = function(channel, pulse) {
   var pulseLength;
   pulseLength = 1000000;
   pulseLength /= 60;
   print("%d us per period" % pulseLength);
   pulseLength /= 4096;
   print("%d us per bit" % pulseLength);
   pulse *= 1000;
   pulse /= pulseLength;
   return pwm.setPWM(channel, 0, pulse);
};
//set pulse frequency
pwm.setPWMFreq(60);
//Make a web server on port 8080
var file = new(static.Server)();
function handler(request, response) {
   console.log('serving file',request.url)
   file.serve(request, response);
};
```

```
console.log('Pi Car we server listening ↵
on port 8080 visit http://ipaddress:8080/ ↵
socket.html');

lastAction = "";
function emergencyStop(){
  //center front wheels
    pwm.setPWM(0, 0, 400);
  //stop motor
    pwm.setPWM(1, 0, 330);
    console.log('###EMERGENCY STOP - signal ↵
lost or shutting down');
}

if (argv.beta) {
    console.log("\nPerforming one off servo ↵
position move to: "+argv.beta);
    pwm.setPWM(0, 0, argv.beta);
//using direct i2c pwm module
    pwm.stop();
    return process.exit();
}
if (argv.gamma) {
    console.log("\nPerforming one off servo ↵
position move to: "+argv.gamma);
    pwm.setPWM(1, 0, argv.gamma); //using
direct i2c pwm module
    pwm.stop();
    return process.exit();
}
//fire up a web socket server
io.sockets.on('connection', function (socket)
{
   socket.on('fromclient', function (data) {
   console.log("Beta: "+data.beta+" Gamma:
"+data.gamma);
   //exec("echo 'sa "+data+"' > /dev/
// ttyAMA0", puts);
//using http://electronics.chroma.se/rpisb.php
   //exec("picar.py 0 "+data.beta, puts);
   //using python adafruit module
   pwm.setPWM(0, 0, data.beta);
//using direct i2c pwm module
   pwm.setPWM(1, 0, data.gamma);
//using direct i2c pwm module
   clearInterval(lastAction);
//stop emergency stop timer
   lastAction = setInterval(emergencySt ↵
op,1000);
//set emergency stop timer
   });
});
process.on('SIGINT', function() {
   emergencyStop();
   console.log("\nGracefully shutting down
from SIGINT ↵ (Ctrl-C)");
   pwm.stop();
   return process.exit();
});
```

Xbox Zero arcade

Let's make a self-contained arcade machine out of old
bits of kit, a spare Xbox pad and a Pi Zero!

What you'll need...

Raspberry Pi Zero

Original Xbox controller

Wire cutters

Craft knife

Isopropyl alcohol swabs

Micro SD card

BluTak

Micro USB OTG cable

Cross-head screwdriver

Electrical tape

2A micro USB power supply

Mini HDMI cable/adapter

The Raspberry Pi Zero is tiny, ridiculously tiny. It's also small enough
to be hidden in a variety of household objects in order to enhance
their capabilities. Whatever you can find to fit it in, you can turn into
some kind of smart machine.

Take old game controllers. If you're anything like us you've
probably got a couple of boxes full of old computer equipment
you just can't bear to throw away – an Atari Jaguar that hasn't been
touched since the 90s, a Sega Dreamcast which you're sure you'll
plug in again one day, an old Xbox that lies languishing since you
picked up something bigger and better. Turns out it actually was
useful to keep them around – it's time to bring these old systems
back to life.

We're going to show you how to gut an old videogames
controller, replace its innards with a Raspberry Pi Zero, and then
load it up with a treasure trove of retro games. From start to finish,
this project should take you under an hour to complete – and then
you'll be able to load up the ROMs you legally own on your new
console and enjoy them from the comfort of your sofa.

Gather your equipment

01 While the Zero doesn't take up much space, videogame controllers are often stuffed full of delicate electronics. The trick here is to find a games controller which has enough space inside for the Zero. We're going to be using the original Xbox controller, nicknamed The Duke. If you don't have one to hand, they can be picked up for a couple of quid from most second-hand electronics shops, and they're easily found online too.

If you can't find one, you can use newer USB game pads that are designed to look like controllers for classic systems like the SNES and Mega Drive. Make sure you choose a controller that has enough buttons for the games you want to play – some classic fighting games, for example, really can't be played on a two-button NES controller.

Warning!

02 Working with electrical items and sharp objects can be dangerous. You risk damaging yourself or, worse, breaking your toys. Please ensure everything is unplugged from electrical supplies before attempting this project. As with any electronics projects, you should also take care to fully ground yourself before playing around with sensitive components –the static electricity from your body can ruin them. Anti-static wrist straps or a few taps on a radiator should do the trick.

Above You can mod your controller with just a few simple tools

Xbox Zero arcade

Right Be careful that you don't lose any small parts when opening up the controller

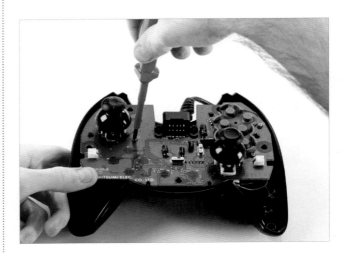

The build

03 You should be now have a reasonably good idea of the controller that we'll be working with. 'The Duke' has dual joysticks, six buttons, a D-Pad and two triggers – and it's compatible with most retro games systems.

Fitting

04 If you're using a different controller, double-check that the Pi is likely to fit inside before you crack it open. As you'll see here, the Pi nestles neatly between the triggers of this controller – the original Xbox controller is one of the largest.

Unscrewing

05 The controller is held together by half a dozen cross-head screws. Be careful when opening the case as the buttons and rubber contacts are loose within the controller – they will spill everywhere!

Opening

06 With the shell removed, you should be able to undo the screws holding the main circuit board in place. There are also a couple of connectors which power the vibration motors – gently unclip them in order to completely remove the board. You might find it easier to use a pair of pliers for this – just be very gentle as you pull!

Gently does it

07 You can see for yourself just how well the Pi fits here; it can be squeezed under the memory card slot. If you want to hold it firmly in place, use some BluTak as a temporary solution. Also, if you're using an older controller, it's worth giving it a bit of a clean. Remove the rubber contacts and gently swab under them using the isopropyl alcohol swabs.

Cut to fit

08 Depending on the model of controller, you may find that the Pi blocks one of the internal plastic struts. The plastic is soft enough that a craft knife will easily cut it down to size, though. Start with small strokes, shaving off a tiny bit at a time until you have enough room. Make sure the plastic dust is cleaned out before you reassemble the controller. If you have a can of compressed air, you can use it to easily blow away the shavings.

Connecting it up

09 If you're using a controller that has a regular USB port on it, you can just plug it into the Pi via a USB OTG converter. If you're using the original Xbox Controller, it's slightly tricky. Microsoft, in its infinite wisdom, has decided that the original Xbox should use USB – but with an incompatible plug design. This means, in order to connect the controller to the Pi, we need to do some wire stripping. Fun!

The wiring inside the Xbox controller's cable uses bog-standard USB wiring colours, so once you've chopped the plugs off the controller and the OTG cable, it's pretty straightforward to connect them together.

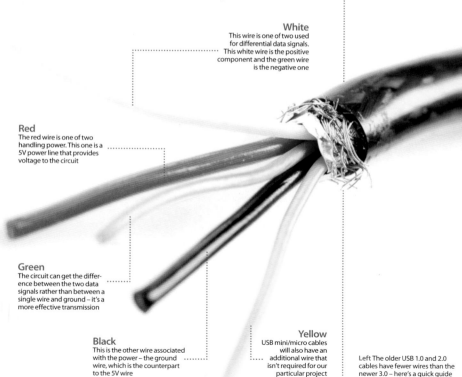

White
This wire is one of two used for differential data signals. This white wire is the positive component and the green wire is the negative one

Red
The red wire is one of two handling power. This one is a 5V power line that provides voltage to the circuit

Green
The circuit can get the difference between the two data signals rather than between a single wire and ground – it's a more effective transmission

Black
This is the other wire associated with the power – the ground wire, which is the counterpart to the 5V wire

Yellow
USB mini/micro cables will also have an additional wire that isn't required for our particular project

Left The older USB 1.0 and 2.0 cables have fewer wires than the newer 3.0 – here's a quick guide

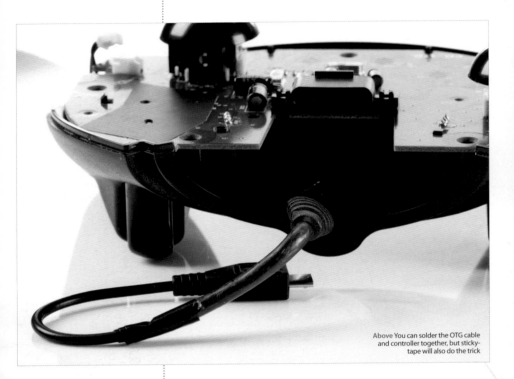

Above You can solder the OTG cable and controller together, but sticky-tape will also do the trick

The right controller

Second-hand stores like CEX or GAME often have some older, obsolete consoles and accessories out of public view, as they aren't particularly high-selling these days. It's worth asking the staff what they have if you can't see what you need on display. Some charity shops also have old consoles for sale. Failing that, local car boot sales or simply asking your gamer friends are both excellent ways to grab inexpensive controllers for all sorts of consoles.

Wiring

10 Strip the wires by a couple of centimetres and then connect them together. You should have Red, Green, White, and Black. The Xbox cable also has a Yellow wire which you can ignore. It is worth noting at this point that you need to be sure that you have a USB data transfer cable and not just a plain old power cable – the former will look like the photo above, but power cables will be missing the two data wires.

With the wires stripped, we temporarily used regular sticky-tape to make the connections between the OTG cable and the controller – for a more permanent installation, you can use electrical tape or simply solder the wires together.

Insulation

11 One thing to note: you'll need to insulate the bottom of the Pi against all the contacts on the controller. For this quick hack, we've used some of the cardboard packaging – but any non-conductive material will do.

From there, it's as simple as screwing the case back together. Make sure that the controller's buttons and joysticks don't slip out of alignment. Keep track of which coloured buttons go where and you should be fine.

Wiring up

12 The Pi will need three wires connected to it in order to work. The controller cable needs to be connected to the USB OTG port. An HDMI cable goes from your TV to the mini HDMI port on the Pi. Finally, a 2A micro USB power supply needs to be plugged into the Pi's power socket. We've used a standard mobile phone charger, but you can use a USB battery pack if you want to reduce the number of wires trailing around your room.

A word about power

13 You might be wondering whether it's possible to get the HDMI cable to supply power from the TV to the controller. Sadly, the HDMI specification doesn't permit power to flow in that direction. If your TV has a USB socket on it, you could use that to supply the Pi with power – just make sure the socket itself is powerful enough. The Pi needs at least 1 Amp, and ideally 2 Amps. Many TVs will only output 500mA which isn't enough to run the Pi.

Let's play!

14 Okay, It's looking good – you're nearly ready to play. The next step is to get some emulation software on this thing.

"If your TV has a USB socket, you could use that to supply the Pi with power – just make sure it's powerful enough"

What's an emulator?

An emulator is software which lets your computer pretend to be a different sort of computer. It will allow a Raspberry Pi Zero to run software originally designed for the Sega Mega Drive, or Nintendo N64, old DOS-based PCs, etc. Emulators aren't without their problems, though – it's nearly impossible to perfectly recreate a games console in software. Keep in mind that older games may have bugs ranging from minor sound and graphical glitches to full-blown crashes.

Installing the RetroPie emulator

It's not as difficult as you might think to run retro software through an emulator

Right, so you've managed to get your Pi safely ensconced in a controller and all wired up – all you need now are some videogames to play.

For this section of the tutorial we're going to be using the RetroPie emulator. By the end of this tutorial, you'll be able to play a number of games directly from your Raspberry Pi, provided that you legally own the ROM files, of course.

The whole process is as easy as installing the software onto your SD card and then copying across any games that you want to play. If you've already got Raspian installed on your Pi, you can install RetroPie alongside it – or you can dedicate the whole disk to the software if you'd rather.

Install RetroPie inside Raspbian

01 If you've already started using your Pi and want to add RetroPie to it, you'll need to install the software from GitHub. The latest instructions can be found at **github.com/RetroPie/RetroPie-Setup**.

Open up a terminal on your Pi (for example, by SSHing into it from another machine, or by logging in directly to the Pi). Update your repositories and make sure the latest version of the Git software is installed:

```
sudo apt-get update
sudo apt-get upgrade
sudo apt-get install git
```

Download the latest version of the RetroPie setup script:

```
git clone --depth=1 https://github.com/RetroPie/RetroPie-Setup.git
```

If you're security-conscious, it's a good idea to check what the script does before running it. Once you're ready, you can install it by changing into the correct directory and executing the script:

```
cd RetroPie-Setup
sudo ./retropie_setup.sh
```

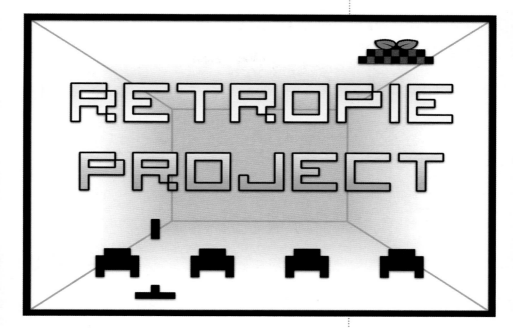

The script will take several minutes to run, depending on the speed of your internet connection. It may also ask you for permission to install extra software that is needed – you should allow this. Once fully installed, you will need to reboot your Pi:

Above If you see a splash screen like this when you power on again, the installation worked!

```
sudo reboot
```

RetroPie can now be run by typing emulationstation. We'll come on to configuring your setup in just a moment.

Install RetroPie onto a blank SD card

02 If you want your Raspberry Pi Zero to be used solely as a RetroPie machine, this is the choice for you. Be warned: it will completely wipe a micro SD card, so if you're using one you've used before, make sure you back up any important data before starting.

Download the latest version of the software from **http://blog.petrockblock. com/retropie/retropie-downloads**. Make sure you download the correct SD card image for your machine – the image for the Raspberry Pi 2 is not compatible with the Raspberry Pi Zero. Download the Standard version (not the BerryBoot version). The download is an 800MB .gz file. Unzip it and extract the .img file, which will be around 2.6GB.

You'll now need to write this image file onto your micro SD card. This is done in the same way that you would install a normal Raspberry Pi image onto a card. There are slightly different instructions for Linux, Mac and Windows.

Installing the RetroPie emulator

Linux

03 Use the Disk Manager to select the image file and the micro SD card. Follow the on-screen instructions until the image has been fully written to the card.

Mac

04 Download the ApplePi Baker from **www.tweaking4all. com/hardware/raspberry-pi/ macosx-apple-pi-baker**. Once you have it installed, you can select the image file and the micro SD card. Follow the on-screen instructions.

Windows

05 Download the Win32 DiskImager from http:// sourceforge.net/projects/ win32diskimager. Once installed, select the image file and the micro SD card. Follow the instructions until the image has been written to the card.

Configuring

06 Right – you're almost ready to play. Put the micro SD card into the Raspberry Pi Zero, hook up the controller USB cable and the HDMI cable. Finally, plug the Pi into the power. It should boot up automatically and, after a few seconds, you'll be greeted with a configuration screen.

RetroPie should automatically detect any connected USB game pads and step you through setting up the buttons. Once you've finished, you'll be presented with a screen showing all the choices you made.

Below RetroPie can be restored straight to SD if you don't need Raspbian as well

Set up the disk

07 Before we get to playing any games, we need to make sure that RetroPie is able to use all the space on the micro SD card. This will allow you to store ROMs and save your games. Select 'RetroPie' from the menu. You'll be presented with several configuration options. Select "Raspberry Pi Configuration Tool RASPI-CONFIG"

You can change the default username and password at a later date; for now just use the controller to select 'Expand Filesystem'. Next, highlight the 'Select' button and click on it. After a short delay, you will see a success screen – press OK and you'll be taken to the configuration screen. Press right until 'Finish' is highlighted, then click on it. You should now reboot your Raspberry Pi.

Adding ROMs

08 The final step is adding new ROMs. Once you've legally purchased and downloaded ROMs from the internet, you'll need to copy them onto the micro SD card. ROMs are stored in a separate folder for each system. So, for example, you need to place your Sega Master System ROMs in ~/RetroPie/roms/mastersystem/. Once you've installed ROMs, you're ready to play.

Playing

09 Once booted, you'll see a menu with all the available games systems on it. Some emulators will only show up once game ROMs for that system are installed. Scroll until you find the game you want to play – then let rip!

You can always return back to RetroPie if you want to change any of the configuration options, or update the software. And that's all there is to it! Time to sit back and play some games. If you want to find out more about the RetroPie software, visit **http://blog. petrockblock.com/retropie**.